Developmental Genetics

Selected Topics in Modern Biology

SERIES EDITOR

Professor Peter Gray
Andrey Avinoff Distinguished Professor of Biology
University of Pittsburgh

Published

Series Editor's Statement

Few branches of biology are so thoroughly intertwined with all the other branches as is genetics today. This new addition to Reinhold's SELECTED TOPICS IN MODERN BIOLOGY explores, coherently and succinctly, one of the most important of these interactions—that is, the role played by genetics in the development of form and function.

Professor Gottlieb deals first with the developmental aspects of his subject, beginning with a rather brief survey of that descriptive embryology which is basic to the understanding of all development and continuing in more detail with functional, or as it is more popularly called, experimental embryology. From this basis, he then passes to the gene, fundamental to the transmission of all characteristics, including those which shape the destinies of cells and organisms. This occupies two chapters, the first of which deals with the gene itself and the second with the mode of action of the gene. In conclusion, he integrates all that has gone before into a coherent picture of "developmental genetics."

This book will serve a dual need. It will introduce developmental genetics to those to whom this is a new concept, and it will augment the knowledge of those whose textbooks slight this important subject.

PETER GRAY

Developmental
Genetics

W 99

FREDERICK J. GOTTLIEB

Department of Biology
University of Pittsburgh
Pittsburgh, Pennsylvania

New York
REINHOLD PUBLISHING CORPORATION
Chapman & Hall Ltd., London

To my "academic fathers"
ERNST CASPARI and CURT STERN

Copyright © 1966 by
Reinhold Publishing Corporation
All rights reserved
Library of Congress Catalog Card Number: 66-18493
Printed in the United States of America

To the Student

The often told story about the blind men who each encountered but a single portion of an elephant, and then attempted to describe the whole animal from what they had learned about this one part, concludes: "Each was right and each was wrong." Biologists find themselves in the same position as they attempt to describe their "elephant"—the living organism. Their descriptions are the results of the observations, made from different vantage points, which are then related to past experiences. Unlike the blind men, however, biologists do not just stand firm and disagree. Instead, they try to piece together the many varying observations in the hope that the resulting collage will enable them adequately to describe their "elephant."

Developmental genetics is an approach which is attempting to synthesize just such a clear picture. This book was written to introduce the student to this new area in the young and rapidly growing field of genetics. To aid him in approaching new ideas with the self-confidence which comes from experience, many of the experiments used as examples in the text are already familiar. However, the conclusions drawn from these experiments are new, as they have been extracted from a new collage. It is hoped that this primer will encourage the student to read further in this field.

FREDERICK J. GOTTLIEB

Pittsburgh, Pennsylvania
February, 1966

Contents

chapter one

Introduction

The study of Developmental Genetics covers a small portion of the more encompassing field of Physiological Genetics. While the latter is concerned with all aspects of gene action, the former is concerned specifically with those aspects which are involved in the developmental processes. Thus, developmental genetics may be considered to be a wedding of embryological studies (both descriptive and experimental) and *phenogenetics,* which is the study of the relationships between the genetic constitution (*genotype*) and the resulting physical manifestation of this constitution (*phenotype*).

Man has long been aware of the regularity of developmental processes. Primitive man, as he first domesticated plants and animals, most certainly observed the striking similarities between parents and offspring. Based on these observations, he found that a parent with desirable characteristics could be used to sire offspring bearing these characteristics. Although he was unaware of the mechanisms of the developmental processes, early man knew that a certain number of weeks after the appearance of the inflorescence, the grain would be ripe; that a chick would emerge from the egg in a specific length of time; and that a certain number of moon periods after a woman's abdomen began to swell and breasts grew tender, an infant would be born. Indeed, he realized early the requirement of domesticated animals that there be two parents and some physical union between them before reproduction would occur. Thus, early man was a competent biologist, and although his ability to observe and comprehend the regularity of development was rudimentary, it was probably of highly positive selective value in his evolution.

Components of Development

At the onset, it is necessary that we view this complex process we have called development more carefully so that we may delimit and discuss some of its major component processes. In our discussions of developmental genetics, we shall concentrate on those aspects of development in multi-cellular organisms which are associated with reproduction, the products thereof, and the production of an adult organism. Four major classes of processes interacting with one another make up the complex process of development: genetic replication, growth, cellular differentiation, and histo- and organogenesis.

1. Genetic replication. This is the means by which the sets of genetic information, genes in chromosomes, are duplicated. The major process involved here is the mitotic cycle. In *mitosis* (discussed in more detail in Chap. 2), a single cell, with its specific set of genetic information, gives rise to two "daughter cells" which are genetically identical to each other and to the cell from which they arose.

2. Growth. This complex process involves the increase in mass of the organism and is intimately associated with cellular metabolic activity. Thus, included in growth are such diverse processes as synthesis, energy utilization, energy storage, catabolic metabolism, and excretion.

3. Cellular Differentiation. This is the process by which cells of common origin, and thus genetically identical, diverge in their structure and/or function and give rise to morphologically and physiologically distinguishable cell lineages. Cell differentiation, some aspects of which are discussed in Chap. 6, is the topic of another book in this series, *Introduction to Cell Differentiation* by Nelson T. Spratt, Jr., to which the reader is referred.

4. Histo- and Organogenesis. These are the processes by which differentiated cells aggregate to form tissues of unitary function. These tissues then associate to make up organs.

Clearly, these processes are intimately interrelated; that is, cellular differentiation presupposes genetic replicative processes, histogenesis and organogenesis presuppose cellular differentiation, and growth presupposes aspects of all of the other processes.

Mode of Attack of the Problem

The *scientific method,* the foundation of the natural sciences, is based primarily upon observation. Methodical observation leads to an accumulation of facts which can then be classified in a logical fashion. Cause-effect relationships can be hypothesized after careful consideration of the organized mass of facts. Controlled experiments are then designed and performed to test an hypothesis. An experimentally supported hypothesis next becomes a theory. The theory is more general in its application and should be predictive in nature. The task facing a scientist might be viewed as one of selecting, observing, and asking the "right" questions of a natural system.

The Big Question

We shall define our natural system as organisms, more specifically for developmental genetics, as the heritable, developmental processes of multicellular organisms. What then are the questions we are going to ask of this system? The "big" question is: How can we reconcile the concomitant uniformity and disparity present in the development of multicellular organisms? This question arises after consideration of three bodies of observational data: (1) All the thousands of cells of the multicellular organism arise by mitotic divisions of the *zygote,* the single cell resulting from the fusion of two gametes. These divisions yield genetically identical cells. (2) In a specific and highly predictable, non-random fashion, adjacent genetically identical cells, in the course of development, give rise to morphologically, physiologically, and biochemically distinct cell lineages and thereby to tissues and organs. (3) Within a species, development proceeds in a precise and regular fashion, resulting in individuals having not only the general morphological, physiological, and biochemical features of the species, but also many of the individual peculiarities of their parents. Let us then subdivide the "big" question into two smaller and more specific questions:

1. How do adjacent genetically identical cells give rise to cell lines that are morphologically, physiologically, and biochemically different?

2. What role do the genes play in the mechanisms controlling development?

In the following chapters, we shall discuss information bearing on these two questions. Using the technique of "divide and conquer," we shall continue to subdivide the questions into numerous limited queries, answer each as well as possible with the information presently available, and then piece together an answer to the "big" question.

chapter two

Development—Descriptive Embryology

In sexually reproducing organisms, development—in the broadest sense—starts before fertilization, at the time of gametogenesis. Indeed, much of the subsequent development of the zygote will depend upon the structure, physiology, and biochemistry of the gametes which have joined to form it. So, let us start our discussion of descriptive embryology with a description of a prime feature of gametogenesis, meiosis. For convenience and clarity, we will discuss the regular cell division mechanism, mitosis, at the same time.

Mitosis and Meiosis

The great majority of sexually reproducing, multicellular organisms are *diploid* through most of their life cycle; that is, each cell nucleus (with exceptions which will be discussed later) has a fixed number of pairs of morphologically identical, homologous chromosomes. The number of pairs (which is referred to as the *haploid* number, or *n*, whereas the number of chromosomes is referred to as the diploid number, or $2n$) is a species specific characteristic and is constant within a given species. *Sexual reproduction* involves the fusion of two *gametes* (sex cells) to form the zygote. There is a process in the formation of gametes which insures the consistency of the $2n$ number of chromosomes in the zygote

Mitosis   Meiosis

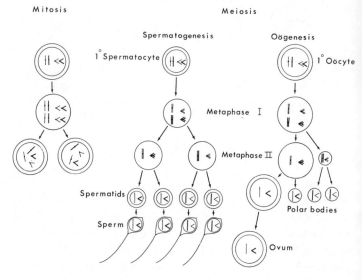

Fig. 2-1. Comparison of mitosis and meiosis.

despite the fusion of two nuclei at fertilization. This process
is the specialized type of cell division known as meiosis.
Unlike mitosis, which gives rise to two daughter cells with
chromosome complements identical to that of the original
cell, meiosis produces cells each of which has half the number of chromosomes of the parent cell, with one member of
each pair of homologues being represented. In Fig. 2-1, the
two types of division, mitosis and meiosis, are diagrammed
side by side. Basically, *mitosis* is a chromosomal replication
followed by an equational nuclear division and a cytoplasmic division. *Meiosis* is a single chromosomal replication
followed by two nuclear and cytoplasmic divisions.

At *metaphase* in mitosis, each pair of *chromatids* (the old
chromosome and its new replicate) lines up on the medial
plate of the spindle. During *anaphase,* the replicated centromere separates into two so that one chromatid of each pair

moves to each pole. Thus, in a diploid cell $(2n = 4)$ from the hypothetical organism shown in Fig. 2-1, four pairs of chromatids line up at metaphase. Each daughter cell nucleus receives one member of each pair, thus maintaining the $2n$ chromosome number of 4.

In metaphase I of meiosis, we find that homologous pairs of chromatids themselves are paired, forming tetrads (associations of four chromatids) which are aligned on the medial plate. In the first meiotic division there is no centromere division, and one pair of chromatids from each tetrad migrates to each pole, yielding two cells, the so-called secondary spermatocytes or secondary oöcytes, each having n pairs of chromatids. There ensues a second division, mitotic in nature but without an intervening chromosome replication, in which one member of each of these pairs of chromatids migrates to each pole, producing cells having a haploid set of chromosomes. In typical spermatogenesis, each primary spermatocyte $(2n)$ yields four spermatids (n) which then develop into spermatozoa. In oögenesis, each primary oöcyte gives rise to one oötid (which then develops into the ovum) and three nonfunctional polar bodies.

Gametogenesis

The meiotic process described above is a small, but most important, part of gametogenesis. In the gonads there are numerous specialized cells which are associated with and contribute to the complex differentiation in which the products of meiosis are converted into mature gametes.

Spermatogenesis and Oögenesis. In animals, the spermatids and oötids mature into spermatozoa and ova, respectively. The appearance of the differentiating sperm of *Drosophila melanogaster* at several stages is illustrated in Fig. 2-2. The main features of the development of the egg of *Drosophila melanogaster* within an ovariole are diagrammatically represented in Fig. 2-3.

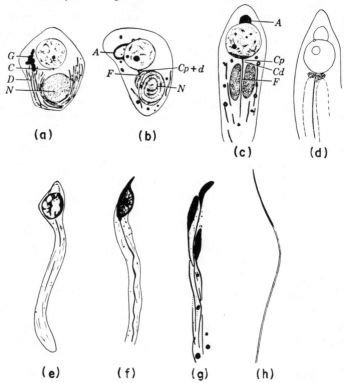

Fig. 2-2. Spermiogenesis in *Drosophila melanogaster*. (a) Early spermatid, (b) Stage of initial elongation of spermatid, (c) Elongating spermatid with fully formed acroblast, (d) Apical end of liver spermatid showing characteristic acroblast, (e) Condensation of chromatin along one side of nucleus, (f) Further nuclear condensation, (g) Three advanced spermatids, (h) Head and first portion of mature sperm; full representation of missing tail portion at this scale would require an additional length of more than 13 feet. N, nebenkern or mitochondrical mass; G, Golgi bodies; C, centriole; Cp, proximal centriole; Cd, distal centriole; D, ductyosomes; A, acroblast; F, axial filament. (From *Biology of Drosophila*, by K. W. Cooper, M. Demerec, ed., 1950, by courtesy of John Wiley & Sons, Inc., N.Y.)

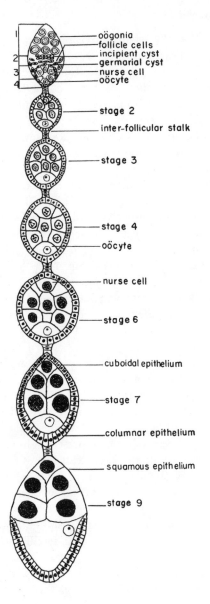

oögonia
follicle cells
incipient cyst
germarial cyst
nurse cell
oöcyte

stage 2

inter-follicular stalk

stage 3

stage 4
oöcyte

nurse cell

stage 6

cuboidal epithelium

stage 7

columnar epithelium

squamous epithelium

stage 9

Fig. 2-3. Diagrammatic representation of main features of oögenesis in an ovariole of *Drosophila melanogaster.* (From Fig. 1, K. S. Gill, 1963, *J. Exp. Zool.,* 152, p. 252.)

It should be noted that the meiotic division does not always initiate gametogenesis. In *Drosophila,* for example, the first meiotic division is in progress at the time of fertilization. The spindle lies close to the dorsal surface of the egg, about one-third of the distance from the anterior end. The long axis of the spindle is oriented perpendicular to the surface (Fig. 2-4a). The sperm pronucleus positions itself near the medial end of the spindle (Fig. 2-4b). The second meiotic division ensues, with the same orientation of the spindles (Fig. 2-4c). During this division haploid complements are formed. Three of the resulting four haploid nuclei become polar body nuclei and move toward the surface of the egg; the fourth becomes the egg pronucleus and associates with the sperm pronucleus with which it will subsequently fuse and form the zygote nucleus (Fig. 2-4d).

Microsporogenesis. In the flowering plants, *microsporogenesis* is the equivalent of spermatogenesis in animals, and megasporogenesis is the equivalent of oögenesis. In *microsporogenesis,* a diploid pollen mother cell gives rise, by meiosis, to four haploid microspores, each of which differentiates into pollen grains. The major features of microsporogenesis are illustrated in Fig. 2-5. In the lower plants a uninucleate motile sperm is formed (Fig. 2-5a). In the gymnosperms, after several divisions, the immature microspore has a number of small "cells" packed at one end and one large cell (Fig. 2-5b). The small cells represent remnants of the gametophyte generation; the large cell corresponds to the young microspore of the angiosperms (Fig. 2-5c) and follows the same course of maturation. The single nucleus divides to form two nuclei, the sperm or generative nucleus and the tube nucleus. The generative nucleus divides again to form two sperm nuclei, one of which will fertilize the ovum, the other, the endosperm.

Megasporogenesis. In megasporogenesis, the formation of the ovum is combined with the development of the embryo

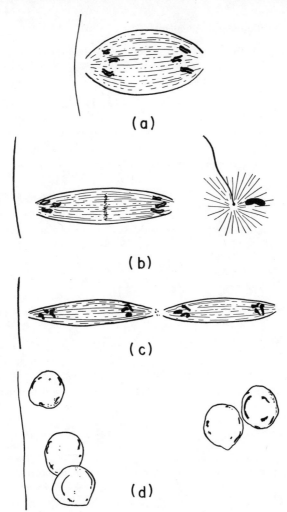

Fig. 2-4. Meiosis in the egg of *Drosophila melanogaster;* line on the side represents egg surface; (a) anaphase of first meiotic division shortly after entrance of spermatozoa, (b) telophase of first meiotic division with sperm head, centriole and aster, (c) anaphase of second meiotic division, (d) polar pronuclei (left), egg and sperm pronuclei (right) before fusion, three polar-body nuclei at egg periphery (left). (From *Biology of Drosophila* by B. P. Sonnenblick, M. Demerec, ed., 1950, by courtesy of John Wiley & Sons, Inc., N.Y.)

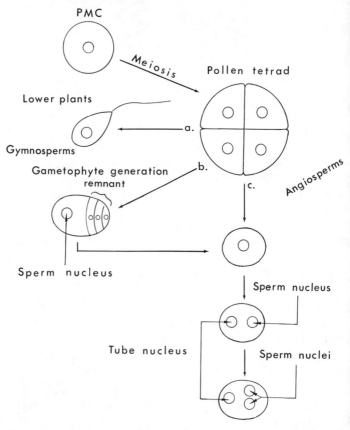

Fig. 2.5. Features of microsorogenesis. The haploid microspores resulting from meiosis in pollen mother cell give rise to uninucleate sperm in lower plants (a) or pollen grain in gymnosperms (b) and angiosperms (c).

sac in which are found elements which will contribute to the nutrition of the forming embryo. A typical megasporogenesis, that of a lily, is illustrated in Fig. 2-6. Within the ovule is located the large megasporocyte, the nucleus of which undergoes the first meiotic division, the reductional division, to produce the two nucleus stage (Fig. 2-6a). Each of these nuclei are referred to as secondary megasporocytes. The second meiotic division, the so-called equational division, occurs with its spindles oriented at right angles to the orientation of the initial division. The result of this second division is a four nucleus stage, the nuclei being referred to as megaspores. The nuclei migrate and reorient in a diamond pattern (as seen in Fig. 2-6c). At this stage, we have four haploid nuclei present. Three of these nuclei, the *chalazal megaspores,* move together and fuse. In Fig. 2-6d we see these three nuclei just prior to the fusion. Now we have two nuclei present, one haploid and one triploid (Fig. 2-6e). Each of these nuclei divides twice, yielding an 8-nucleate stage with four haploid and four triploid nuclei (Fig. 2-6f). One haploid nucleus enlarges and becomes the egg nucleus, two of the remaining haploid nuclei become the so-called synergids and orient themselves on each side of the egg nucleus. The fourth haploid migrates to the center of the embryo sac and fuses with one of the triploid nuclei to form the endosperm nucleus. The remaining three triploid nuclei locate themselves at the opposite end of the embryo sac from the ovum and become the three antipoles which are separated from the rest of the cytoplasm and nuclei by a thin cell wall. The mature embryo sac thus formed is surrounded by diploid ($2n$) integument tissue. In the process of fertilization, the pollen grain produces a pollen tube which migrates down through the pistil and passes through the micropile (which is adjacent to the egg nucleus end of the embryo sac). The two sperm nuclei enter the embryo sac and a double fertilization occurs. One of the sperm nuclei fuses with the egg nucleus to form the zygote nucleus, and the other fuses with the endosperm nucleus to form the *polyploid endosperm.* Thus, in plants, fertilization involves not only the formation of a diploid zygote, but also the formation of the polyploid endosperm which will surround the zygote in the seed.

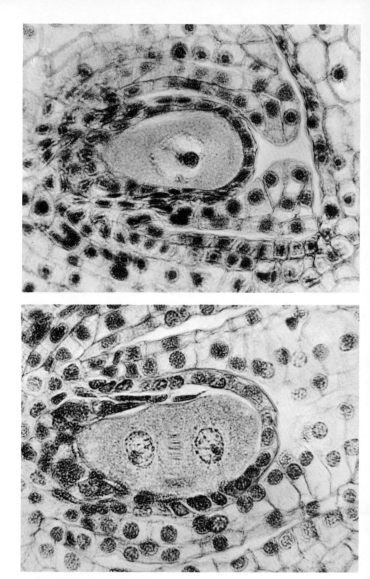

Fig. 2-6. Megasporogenesis in the lily; (a) cross section through embryo sac with megasporocyte about to undergo division, (b) secondary megasporocytes, the 2-nucleate stage, (c) 1st. 4-nucleate stage with nuclei (megaspores) arranged in the diamond-shaped pattern preceding migra-

14

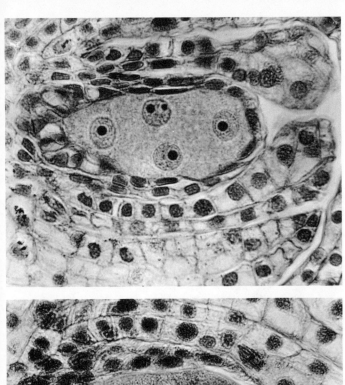

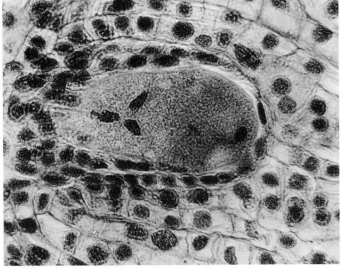

tation of the three chalayal nuclei, (d) stage just before fusion of the three chalayal megaspores, (e) anaphase of the third division, (f) 8-nucleate stage. (Photographs courtesy of John Limbach, Ripon Microslides Laboratory, Ripon, Wisconsin.)

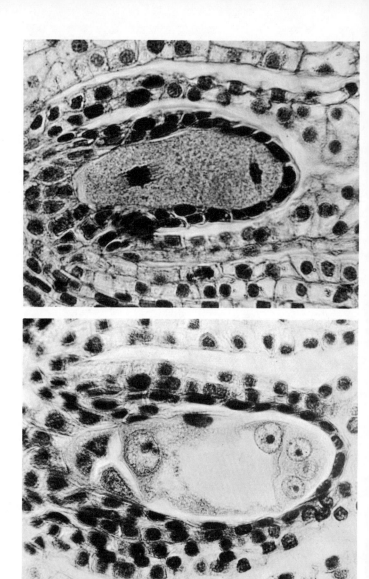

Fig. 2-6. *(cont.)*

Initiation of Embryogenesis in Animals

The completion of fertilization and the initiation of embryo development is marked by the fusion of the two haploid pronuclei to form a single diploid nucleus. The resulting cell contains an equal genetic contribution from each of its parents and, within its mass of cytoplasm, many additional components from its mother. Initial multicellularity is then accomplished by a number of mitotic divisions and the associated process of *cytokinesis* (cytoplasmic division). These initial divisions, when they occur in animals, are referred to as cleavage.

In animal zygotes, the nature of the cleavage divisions is mechanically affected by the distribution of stored nutrient (or yolk) material in the egg and is dynamically affected by the orientation of spindles during the mitotic divisions.

Yolk Distribution in Eggs. There are three major classes of egg types, distinguished by their yolk distribution.

1. *Isolecithal* (Gr. *isos,* equal + *lekithos,* yolk). In this type of egg, the yolk material is sparse and uniformly distributed throughout the egg cytoplasm.

2. *Telolecithal* (Gr. *telos,* end). There is a large quantity of yolk in these eggs, with an accumulation at one end of the egg.

3. *Centrolecithal* (Gr. *kentron,* center). There is also a large quantity of yolk material in these eggs, but it is aggregated in the center of the egg with the egg cytoplasm surrounding it.

Basic Cleavage Patterns. Each of these types of eggs is usually associated with a specific type of cleavage.

1. *Holoblastic* (Gr. *holos,* whole + *blastos,* germ). In this type of cleavage, the cleavage furrows cut completely through the egg. Holoblastic cleavages are characteristic of isolecithal eggs.

2. *Meroblastic* (Gr. *meros,* part). Meroblastic cleavages are characteristic of telolecithal eggs, in which the yold is accumulated at one end, the vegetal pole, and relatively absent from the other, the animal pole. The cleavage furrows cut completely through the animal pole, but incompletely or not at all through the vegetal pole, depending on the size of the yolk mass.

3. *Superficial* (L. *super,* above + *facies,* face). Superficial cleavage is characteristic of forms having centrolecithal eggs, such as the insects. Here, the early divisions occur only in the surface layer of the egg, and do not extend into the central yolk mass.

Representative Animal Cleavages

The Holoblastic Pattern. The cleavage of the sea urchin egg, typical of the holoblastic pattern found in isolecithal eggs, such as those of echinoderms, is shown in Fig. 2-7. The fertilized egg (a) has a central nucleus and a cytoplasm with little yolk. The first cleavage (b) is longitudinal; that is, the spindle is oriented with its long axis in the

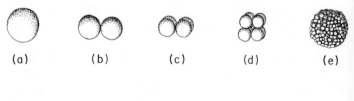

(a)   (b)   (c)   (d)   (e)

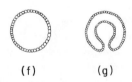

(f)   (g)

Fig. 2-7. Holoblastic cleavage in the isolecithal egg of a sea urchin. (From *General Zoology,* by Goodnight, Goodnight and Gray, 1964, Reinhold, N.Y.)

equatorial plane. The second cleavage divisions (c) are also longitudinal and at right angles to the first cleavage. The third cleavage divisions (d) are equatorial; that is, the spindles have their long axis oriented perpendicular to the equator.

As the cleavages continue (e), the number of cells increases, the synchrony of division ceases, and a solid sphere of cells is formed, the *morula*. The cells continue to divide, a cavity forms within the morula, and finally the *blastula*, a single cell-layered hollow sphere is formed (g). Continued cell division next leads to gastrulation and to subsequent evolution of the three tissue layers—ectoderm, mesoderm, and endoderm.

The Meroblastic Pattern. In the meroblastic cleavage of the frog egg (Fig. 2-8), which is moderately telolecithal, the high concentration of yolky material in the vegetal half of the egg (a) retards the progress of the cleavage furrow (b) so that the second division begins before the first is completed (c). After the first two longitudinally oriented cleavages, the third is "equatorial" in orientation, but it occurs above the equatorial midline, producing two different cell

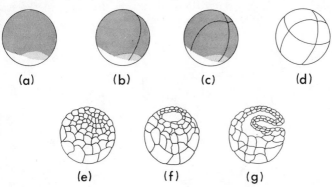

(a)   (b)   (c)   (d)

(e)   (f)   (g)

Fig. 2-8. Meroblastic cleavage in the telolecithal egg of a frog. (Modified from *General Zoology,* by Goodnight, Goodnight and Gray, 1964, Reinhold, N.Y.)

sizes—small animal pole cells, *micromeres,* and large vegetal pole cells, *macromeres* (d).

The subsequent divisions proceed more rapidly in the yolk free animal pole cells than in the yolk laden vegetal pole cells and lead to the formation of morula which has a large number of small cells in the animal half and a smaller number of large cells in the vegetal half (e). The blastocoel, the cavity of the blastula, forms internally between the animal and vegetal pole cells (f). Gastrulation is initiated by an involution at a particular locus on the surface (the dorsal lip of the blastopore) as the result of the animal pole cells overgrowing the vegetal pole cells (g). It is within this dorsal lip region that the mesoderm will arise.

The Superficial Pattern. We will use *Drosophila mela-nogaster* to illustrate the superficial cleavage pattern associated with the centrolecithal egg (Fig. 2-9). The egg of *Drosophila* is encased by two envelopes, the tough opaque outer membrane, the *chorion,* and the inner, transparent *vitelline membrane.* There are numerous yolk masses distributed throughout the cytoplasm except for the thin cortical layer of yolk free cytoplasm and the clear cytoplasmic island in which occurs the maturation divisions of the egg

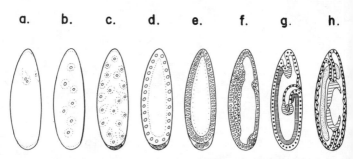

Fig. 2-9. Superficial cleavage in the centrolecithal egg of *Drosophila.* (From Scriba, M., *Zool. Jb. Anat.* **81**, pp. 435–490, 1964.)

nucleus. Upon insemination, the sperm nucleus moves into the cytoplasmic island (Fig. 2-9a). After the second meiotic division of the egg nucleus is completed, the sperm and egg nuclei fuse and the early cleavage nuclear divisions occur synchronously within the clear cytoplasmic island (Fig. 2-9b). The yolk nuclei and the pole nuclei, which are the first to depart from division synchrony, move posteriorly. The embryo at this stage is still *syncytial;* that is, it is multinucleate with no membranes delimiting single cells (Fig. 2-9c). The synchronous nuclear divisions continue until, at about the 4100 cell stage, there is formed a narrow, cytoplasmic layer densely packed with nuclei, the *blastema,* surrounding the central yolk mass (Fig. 2-9d). The pole nuclei form the pole cells, and will later give rise to the gonads, which are located at the posterior end of the embryo outside the blastema.

With segmentation—the formation of cell boundaries—the blastema becomes the *blastoderm*. Thus, about three hours after development begins, the embryo is a single layer of columnar cells surrounding a central yolk mass and has a polar cell cap at the posterior end (Fig. 2-9e). The formation of a longitudinal ventral furrow marks the beginning of gastrulation. The cells of the dorsal surface divide and form the germ band. As divisions continue, the pole cells are moved passively anterior, where they associate with the posterior midgut rudiment (Fig. 2-9f). The *stomodaeum* forms as an inpocketing of the anterior surface and the posterior midgut invaginates, carrying the pole cells along with it (Fig. 2-9g). The mesoderm arises, and the complex development into the larva continues.

Secondary Embryogenesis

We must also mention at this point postembryonic embryogenesis. In many organisms there is a marked difference in morphology, physiology, biochemistry, and pattern of behavior between larval (or immature) stages, and adult (or mature) stages. Most organisms which show such marked differences undergo some form of *metamorphosis*. If we examine insects as an example, we find that prior to the actual metamorphosis there are a number of regions of embryonic tissue growing, differentiating, and preparing for their roles as adult organs. Thus, the imaginal discs, which first appear late in embryology and persist throughout larval life, give rise to their particular adult organs by a process best classified as *secondary embryogenesis*.

The Primary Germ Layers

In the *triploblastic* metazoa, early embryology leads to the formation of three germ layers—the ectoderm, the endoderm, and the mesoderm. Cells from each of these layers will, in the course of subsequent development and differentiation, give rise to specific types of tissue in the mature animal. The *ectoderm*, which starts off as the outer layer of the three layered embryo, gives rise to the epidermis, the nervous system, and sensory structures. The *endoderm*, which is associated in early embryology with the forming digestive system, gives rise to the linings of cavities continuous with the outside, such as mouth, lungs, alimentary canal, etc. It is the *mesoderm*, which began as a proliferation of cells between the other two layers, which gives rise to the majority of remaining structures in the organism. Among the tissues in the adult organism which are of mesodermal origin are muscle, the fluid tissue of the blood, glandular tissues, deeper integumentary structures, the coelomic linings of the vascular organs, and the tissues of the excretory and reproductive systems.

Early Embryogenesis in Plants

Let us now return briefly to early embryology of the plant. Such a sequence is illustrated in Fig. 2-10. After fertilization the zygote nucleus forms a cell at one end of the embryo sac (Fig. 2-10a). There follows a sequence of nuclear

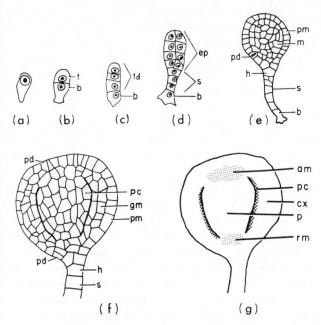

Fig. 2-10. Early embryology of an angiosperm; am = apical meristem, b = basal cell, cx = cortex, ep = embryo proper, gm = ground meristem, h = hypophysis, p = pith, pc = procambium, pd = periclinal division, pm = protoderm, rm = root meristem, s = suspensor, t = terminal cell, td = derivatives. (From Mahlberg, P. G., *Phytomorphology* 10, pp. 118–131, 1960, Figs. 1, 2, 3, 6, 13.)

divisions with the subsequent formation of cells. In the initial divisions (Fig. 2-10b, c), the spindles are oriented parallel to the long axis of the embryo sac, forming a line of four cells. At the same time, the endosperm nucleus continues to divide, yielding a small embryonic mass surrounded by a mass of tissue with a large number of endosperm nuclei. Following this, at the apical end of the zygote, the orientation of the spindles of the subsequent divisions will shift so that they now lie perpendicular to the original axis (Fig. 2-10d). There follows a number of divisions in the apical end forming a ball of cells, while, at the same time, the cells in the basal end continue their pattern of regular linear division so that we find a structure that very much resembles a lollipop—a ball of cells at the end of a long line of cells. This lower line of cells is referred to as the *suspensor*. It serves the function of holding the embryo in place in the seed and of connecting the embryo to the nutritive endosperm. The apical ball of cells continues to increase in size (Fig. 2-10e). After a number of additional divisions, the ball of cells at the apical end of the embryo begins to show the initial differentiation into cell types (Fig. 2-10f), beginning with the surface layer of *protoderm* cells. At this time, as in the three germ layer stage in the animal embryo, certain areas of the embryo are predestined to form certain tissues in the mature plant. In Fig. 2-10g, we see represented the areas within the embryo which will give rise to the *apical meristem*—a continuing portion of embryonic tissue which will give rise to a new structural element from the apical end of the stem throughout the life of the plant—to the *root meristem*—which will give rise to root elements throughout the subsequent development of the plant—to the *procambium*—which will give rise to vascular tissue in development—and the *cortex* and *pith* material. Thus, in the development of the plant, as in the development of the animal, the future roles and future differentiation of tissues have been determined and are specific.

Overview

The question we have asked in this chapter is: What is the normal course of events in the embryonic development of a plant or animal? The answers we have provided have been descriptive in nature, yet they form the foundation for subsequent experimental work, as it is necessary to understand the normal events before trying to interpret abnormal sequences.

chapter three

Development—Experimental Embryology

In the last chapter we reviewed the events of normal embryology in several representative organisms. Such a descriptive approach unfortunately yields little information concerning the mechanisms controlling development. Here, as in many areas of biology, abnormalities or malfunctions have been found to be invaluable in delimiting the normal course of events. With the induction and manipulation of such abnormalities, we cross from the field of descriptive embryology into the field of experimental embryology. One can further divide experimental embryology into two general areas of approach: (1) the area which utilizes alterations *in vivo,* such as transplantation of a structure from one part of the embryo to another and (2) the area in which alterations are induced in *in vitro* experiments, usually referred to as organ, tissue, or cell culture. From the standpoint of understanding normal development, the former approach, that of *in vivo* experimentation, has been most rewarding in animal preparations, while the latter has been more rewarding in plant materials.

Is Early Development Predetermined?

Roux' Classical Study. The limitations of descriptive embryology in explaining cause-effect relationships prompted

Wilhelm Roux, in 1885, to initiate a series of experiments which were the forerunners of the field of experimental embryology. Roux called his new approach to embryology "Entwicklungsmechanik" (Developmental mechanics) and proposed that the controlled mechanisms, indeed the details of embryology, could be studied under a controlled experimental approach. Roux' experiments attacked one of the basic problems of cell differentiation; that is, what are the capabilities of the fertilized egg as a whole, or parts of the fertilized eggs, to develop normally in the presence of disruptive environmental factors? He worked with the eggs of the green frog (*Rana esculenta*), which is easily cultured in the laboratory. With a hot needle, he punctured one of the two blastomeres resulting from the first cleavage, thereby killing that cell, and he observed the subsequent differentiation of the zygote. These experiments, Roux felt, should adequately test Weismann's hypothesis of predetermination based upon a fixed arrangement of developmental potentialities within the nucleus of a fertilized egg and a nonrandom distribution of these potentialities to the nuclei resulting from cleavage. In Fig. 3-1 are shown some of the results Roux obtained. The destruction, *in situ,* of one of the two original blastomeres results, after subsequent development, in the formation of a half embryo. Roux concluded from his results that each of the two blastomeres had predetermined potentialities; that is, it was as if the egg were a mosaic of potentialities of which each of the dividing cells received only a small portion of the total. These results seemingly confirmed Weismann's views that the egg was a preformed mosaic of potentialities, but they did not distinguish between differential nuclear divisions and a regional distribution of metabolites within the cytoplasm.

The Problem Revisited. Following in Roux' footsteps, four years later Hans Driesch attacked the same problem using different methods and a different organism. In the

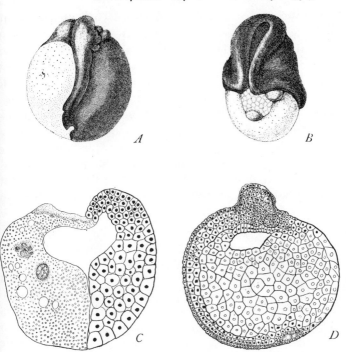

Fig. 3-1. Results of Roux' experiments injuring one of the first two blastomeres. A, typical half-embryo; B, "anterior embryo" after injury to one of the blastomeres in an egg in which the first cleavage was at right angles to medial plane; C, section through blastula stage of developing half-embryo; D, section through half-embryo as shown in A. (From *Experimental Embryology* (Fig. 153) by Morgan, T. H., 1927, by courtesy of Columbia University Press, N.Y.)

eggs of an echinoderm he was able to separate the first blastomeres from one another. He had expected, on the basis of Roux' findings, that each of the separated primary blastomeres would give rise to a half embryo. Instead, he found that each gave rise to a fully developed normal embryo half the size of one developing from an intact egg. Obviously, Driesch could not interpret these results in the same fashion that Roux had interpreted his results. Each of the initial blastomeres had retained its capacity to differentiate into an entire larva. Other factors must have been responsible for the Roux results, because the potency of the nucleus and cytoplasm had not halved with the cleavage division. Indeed, later workers showed that if Roux' experiments were performed again, and if after killing one of the cells the dead one was separated from its partner, the living blastomere would develop into an entire embryo. Thus, the environmental factor of having a dead cell adjacent to a live cell alters the capabilities of the live cell to differentiate in a normal fashion. The live cell, in a sense, "knows" that the

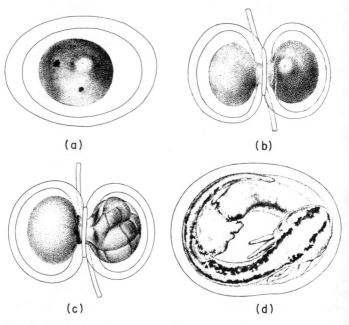

(a)   (b)

(c)   (d)

Fig. 3-2. Spemann's experiments with delayed nucleation of newt egg. See text for description. (From Spemann, H., 1928. *A. fur wissenschaft. Zool.* **132**, pp. 105–134.)

other cell is present and "assumes" that it is taking care of its half of the embryo. When there is no adjacent cell, the blastomere must "assume" it is a zygote and, as such, must start embryogenesis from the beginning.

Delayed Nucleation. In each of the above experiments, the nucleus and cytoplasm were kept in constant contact

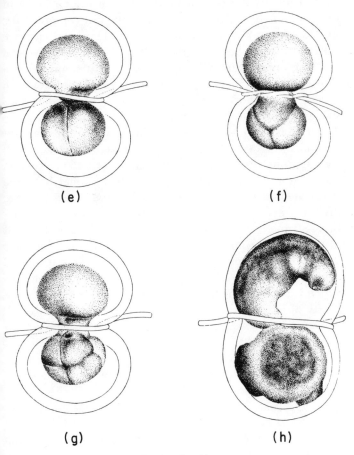

(e)　　　　　　　　(f)

(g)　　　　　　　　(h)

Fig. 3-2. *(cont.)*

and communication and thus were of the same developmental stage. The question of the ability of the nucleus to control the normal functioning of the cytoplasm of a different developmental stage should now be posed. The work of Spemann (in 1925) on the delayed nucleation of egg cytoplasm sheds some light in this area. Spemann found that he could constrict a fertilized newt egg with a loop made of human hair so that only one half of the cell contained the nucleus (Fig. 3-2a). A number of relatively normal cleavage divisions would occur in the half with the nucleus (Fig. 3-2b). If, after an appropriate number of divisions, the tension on the hair loop was relaxed, a nucleus from a first, second, third, fourth, or later cleavage division would pass into the enucleate cytoplasm. If the constriction was *equational,* that is, in a longitudinal plane such as the one that normally separates the first two blastomeres, even a fourth cleavage nucleus, that is, 1/16 of a 16 cell stage embryo, was capable of producing an entire twin animal from the enucleated half (Fig. 3-2c, d). Nuclei from later cleavage divisions were not capable of producing normal twin embryos. If the constriction was not equational, even the half of the egg containing 15 of the 16 cells of a fourth cleavage did not develop into an entire normal embryo, but instead gave rise to a partial embryo. There are two conclusions which can be drawn from Spemann's findings: (1) The capacity of a zygote nucleus in egg cytoplasm to control an entire embryogenesis changes after the nucleus has undergone a number of cleavage divisions; (2) The capability of the zygote nuclei to mediate normal embryogenesis is dependent on the nature of the cytoplasm in which the development takes place.

The Qualitative Role of the Cytoplasm. Similar conclusions as to the role of the cytoplasm can be drawn from the results of a series of surgical experiments in echinoderm eggs. If a fertilized echinoderm egg is cut in half equatorially, thus creating a nucleated animal or vegetal half and an enucleate vegetal or animal half, the subsequent course of development is quite different from that of a zygote cut equationally. In the nucleate half embryo resulting from an equational cut, development proceeds normally, and a typical pluteus larva develops (Fig. 3-3a). Two different types of abnormal larvae develop from the nucleate halves of equatorial cuts, depending on whether the cytoplasm was from the animal or vegetal pole. Halves with animal cytoplasm (Fig. 3-3b) give rise to "animalized" or "ectodermized" ab-

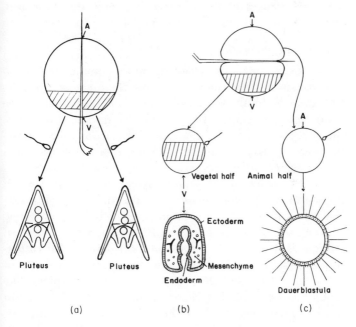

Fig. 3-3. Development of echinoderm embryos from half eggs; normal pluteus larva from equational cut (a), endodermalized (b), and ectodermalized (c) abnormal larvae from equatorial cut. (From Barth, L. G., *Embryology*, 1953, by permission of Holt, Rinehart and Winston, Inc., N.Y.)

normal larvae which, in extreme cases, are uniformly cili-
ated, without skeletal structures, and in which no gastrulation has occurred. Halves with vegetal cytoplasm (Fig. 3-3c)
give rise to "vegetalized" or "endodermized" abnormal larvae which, in extreme cases, contain only gut elements
within an ectodermal vesicle. In all cases, the enucleate half
dies. We can see clearly from these results that it is not the
quantity of cytoplasm which controls the differentiation ca-
pacities of the nucleus but, rather, the quality of the cytoplasm. It is also clear that differentiation involves both the
nucleus and the cytoplasm; that is, as the nucleus differentiates and changes in function, so then does the cytoplasm
change in function as a result of the nuclear changes.

Intercellular Interactions

The experiments described up to this point have been
directed toward questions concerning the capacity of single
cells to undergo differentiation. Let us advance one level in
organizational complexity and consider questions concerning the potentialities of aggregates of cells to differentiate
into specific tissues, and the influence exerted by one such
cell aggregate upon another.

The Transplantation Approach. Spemann had shown in
his constriction experiments that the inclusion of material from one specific cytoplasmic area of the egg, the grey
crescent, was prerequisite to normal development. The grey
crescent is the site of initiation of gastrulation, that is, the
future dorsal lip of the blastopore. This is the area of origin
of the mesoderm and thus the site of primary triploblastic
differentiation. Could it be, Spemann wondered, that cells
from different regions of the blastula were specific in their
capabilities for influencing or even altering the course of
differentiation of other groups of cells? He reasoned that
transplantation, that is, surgical removal of groups of cells
from one area of an early embryo and implantation to the

same or different area of another embryo of the same age, would provide answers to this question. After developing instruments and techniques with which such experimentation could be accomplished, he, and later his students, performed numerous experiments with amphibian embryos.

Presumptive vs. Realized Fate. If a piece of *presumptive* brain tissue (tissue on the surface of a late blastula or early gastrula which will, in undisturbed development, become brain tissue) is transplanted to an area of presumptive epidermis in an embryo of the same stage of development and vice versa, the transplant will differentiate into tissue characteristic of the region into which it was transplanted; that is, the transplanted piece of presumptive brain tissue will become epidermis in a presumptive epidermal area and vice versa. Thus, the course of differentiation in these presumptive areas is not rigidly fixed in the cells. On the contrary, the differentiation path to be followed depends upon the direction of differentiation of the adjacent tissue.

The Primary Organizer. Strikingly different results are obtained when a piece of tissue from the region of the dorsal lip of the blastopore is transplanted into a presumptive epidermal region. Not only does this type of transplant continue in its normal course of differentiation, but the differentiation of the surrounding presumptive epidermis is altered so that it produces a secondary embryo, derived almost entirely from the host tissue.

The dorsal lip of the blastopore represents a center of organization, and the tissue of this region is, as Spemann called it, the primary *"organizer"* of the embryo. The action of the organizer, whereby it determines the course of differentiation of adjacent tissue, is called *induction*. The ability of primary organizer tissue to induce the formation of secondary embryonic primordia is "host-time dependent," that is, dependent upon the developmental stage of the host. If dorsal lip tissue is transplanted into a later stage embryo, such as the "limb bud stage," the transplant gives rise to notochord and somite tissue, but the host tissue continues to develop normally.

Secondary Organizers. There are many examples of tissues acting as secondary organizers in postgastrula development. One such tissue is the forming eye cup which acts as the organizer for the formation of the lens from the adjacent epidermal ectoderm. The sequence of developmental events in this system is illustrated in Fig. 3-4. As the brain develops, the primary optic vesicles come in contact with the epidermal ectoderm of the lateral head surface (Fig. 3-4a). As the optic vesicle continues to develop, an infolding occurs, and the eye cup begins to form (Fig. 3-4b). After the appearance of the eye cup, a thickening of the epidermal layer develops over it (Fig. 3-4c). The thickening invaginates (Fig. 3-4d)

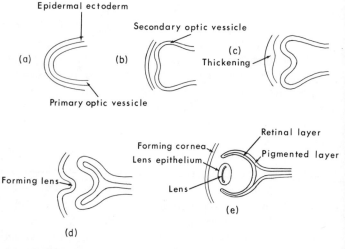

Fig. 3-4. Formation of the lens in the developing vertebrate eye. (Modified from *Comparative Embryology of the Vertebrates,* by Nelson, 1953, McGraw-Hill Book Company, by permission of McGraw-Hill Book Company.)

and finally forms the lens, the lens epithelium (internally), and a reconstituted epidermal layer (Fig. 3-4e). The organizer role of the eye cup has been demonstrated in experiments in which an eye cup was transplanted into an atypical location in an embryo in close proximity to the epidermal layer, such as just below the ectoderm in the abdominal region. In animals receiving such a transplant, a lens differentiates from the overlying epidermal ectoderm in the same fashion as outlined above, resulting in an animal with three eyes, two in their normal cranial location and the third in the abdomen.

Chemical Nature of Induction. The chemical nature of the induction mechanism was revealed when it was found that damaged primary organizer could be effective in its induction capabilities. Holtfreter found that even dorsal lip tissue killed by alcohol was an effective organizer, and, indeed, extracts from various tissues from numerous species were capable of inducing neural tube formation. After this discovery, innumerable experiments were performed in which a vast number of organic and inorganic chemicals were tested for induction activity, showing that a variety of chemically unrelated materials demonstrated such activity. More recently, experiments have confirmed that diffusable inducer substances are produced by primary and secondary organizer tissue.

Reversibility of Cell Differentiation

As we have stated, development and differentiation during embryogenesis are the means by which the single cell zygote is converted into a multicellular organism. One can question whether or not these cell changes are permanent; that is, is cell differentiation an irreversible process? Let us consider an early observation in plant development. If a plant is decapitated (Fig. 3-5a) and the decapitated stem portion is allowed to continue to grow (Fig. 3-5b), there

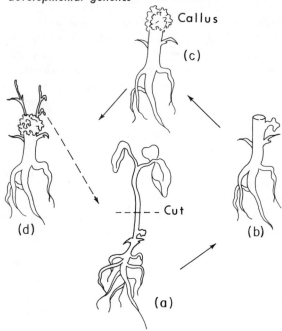

Fig. 3-5. Development of shoots from callus tissue.

soon develops at the cut edge a callus overgrowth (Fig. 3-5c). *Callus* is a mass of relatively undifferentiated tissue. After subsequent growth, shoots regenerate from the callus tissue (Fig. 3-5d). These shoots may be removed from the callus, planted in an appropriate medium, and they will grow into full plants. From observations of this sort, we must conclude that at least some of the cells in the mature differentiated stem retained the potentiality for differentiation. Although they were differentiated with respect to the entire organism (that is, in normal context the position in the plant stem would determine their degree of differentiation), when they were taken out of context, the relationships that defined this context were altered. The conditions which control their differentiation were no longer the same, and the cells were once again able to express their full potentiality for differentiation. In this case, the full potentiality would be the reestablishment of a normal or near normal embryogenetic process and the formation of the entire new shoot. Once again, as in the experiments on animals noted above, there are indications of interactions between cells, interactions which could be termed environmental.

Chemical Factors in Regeneration

If we were able to identify some of the chemical factors controlling differentiation we might well have an explanation for such phenomena as polarity and the difference between anterior and posterior or dorsal and ventral. Jacobs, working with the plant Coleus, demonstrated not only the presence of such a chemical material but also the identity of this material and its point of origin. If a notch is cut through the vascular strand of the stem of Coleus and the plant is allowed to continue to grow, a connection is reestablished between the upper and lower portion of this vascular strand. By differentiation, the cells within the pith that were formerly parenchyma are transformed into new vascular tissue (Fig. 3-6a). If, however, the leaves are removed above the cut, the reestablishment of the vascular strand connection does not occur (Fig. 3-6b). What is it that the leaves produce that would alter this differentiation? Jacobs reasoned that perhaps the auxins which control leaf growth are the factors involved. If this were the case, he reasoned, then supplying the auxins to a plant from which the leaves have been removed should result in the same type of regeneration as would occur if the leaves were present. He experimented with this idea by placing a glob of lanolin containing auxin on the point from which the leaf had been cut (Fig. 3-6c), and, as he had expected, the vascular connection was reestablished (Fig. 3-6d). He also found that in this

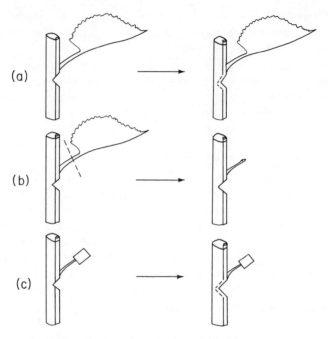

Fig. 3-6. Regeneration of vascular tissue in Coleus.

regenerative process, the response to the auxin was proportional to its concentration and could attain, as a maximum response, the results obtained in the notched stem in the presence of leaves.

Limiting Factors

What is it, then, that limits the expression of a cell or tissue in differentiation; that is, why does presumptive epithelial rarely differentiate into nervous tissue except under certain conditions, and why does the vascular strand in the stem always reestablish the connection when damage is present? The answer to the latter question is quite clear. The amount of auxin present limits the differentiation potential of the parenchyma cells. Auxin, then, is the limiting factor in this particular differentiation. We might consider that all differentiations are limited by the presence of some environmental factors such as precursor materials, inducing agents, growth hormones, etc. If this is the case, the effectiveness of an organizer is thus proportional to its capabilities to provide amounts of limiting factors which enable the induced cells to exhibit the differentiation potential. To further illustrate this principle of limiting factors, let us consider two lines of *in vitro* research. One of these involves culture of animal tissue.

Mutual Induction. In the development of the vertebrate kidney, two cords of mesoderm interact to form the tubules. It is possible to observe tubule development in tissue culture. If cords of the two types of mesoderm are placed in contact with each other and cultured, one cord differentiates into the collecting tubule, which evaginates and induces the other cord to produce the secretory tubule. The two tubules subsequently fuse to form the final kidney tubule. If the two types of mesoderm are cultured separately, they each grow, but neither differentiates into tubules. If the two cords are grown in the same culture but separated by a porous membrane, normal growth and differentiation into tubules occurs. These two sets of observations indicate that each type of mesoderm produces a substance, probably chemical in nature, which is able to traverse a short distance and pass through a porous barrier. While these results indicate a chemical inducer, no chemical extract of either mesoderm was found to induce differentiation in cultures of the complementary type. Thus, the chemical agents in this mutual induction system are probably small molecules, relatively unstable and short lived.

Callus Vascularization. The other experiment performed by Wetmore and his associates involves the proliferation of callus material. As we have mentioned, callus is essen-

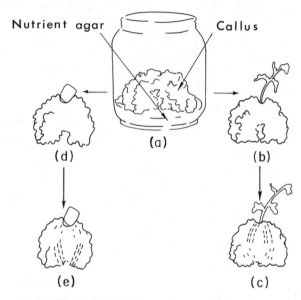

Fig. 3-7. The induction of vascular organization in callus.

tially undifferentiated parenchyma cells. If a mass of callus is grown on a suitable medium, such as nutrient materials in agar, little organized differentiation occurs. Such a mass of callus (Fig. 3-7a), although it has a small amount of unorganized differentiation of vascular cell types, shows no organized vascular bundles. When Wetmore grafted a bud onto the top of such a callus (Fig. 3-7b), and allowed it to continue to grow, he found that beneath the bud there occurred differentiation of vascular elements in an organized fashion somewhat reminiscent of the organization in the developing stem (Fig. 3-7c). Following Jacobs' findings, he redid the experiment, using auxin in lanolin instead of a bud (Fig. 3-7d). Here again (Fig. 3-7e), he found an increase in differentiation in vascular elements. These results serve to emphasize the fact that it was the cells in the callus that maintained their capabilities for differentiation because in the *in vitro* study there was no underlying organized stem for nourishing the callus, only nutrient material in agar medium. One other fact that is made clear by the Wetmore work is that not only is the differentiation of individual elements controlled by the presence of the limiting factor, the auxin in this case, but indeed the pattern of the distribution of these elements is also controlled. The polarity in such an experiment represents not only the position of the cell in the callus, but also the position of the source of the inducing substance and the diffusion gradient produced by this material originating at one point and diffusing out to the surrounding tissue.

Maintenance of Totipotency

We noted earlier in this chapter that the cells from the animal zygote lose their capability to produce intact normal embryos (and thus, normal adults) after a very small number of cleavage divisions. Is this the case in plant tissue? Numerous experiments have been done with plant material in which pieces of mature plant tissue were grown in the appropriate fluid media under agitation. It is possible, by these culture techniques, to isolate a suspension of single cells and small aggregates. Some of these isolated single cells can, if placed on a solid medium, undergo a process very reminiscent of normal embryogeny and develop into entire plants. This type of redevelopment of an embryo from a cell culture has been demonstrated in numerous species. It has led to the general conclusion that at least some of the cells within the mature plant tissue maintained totipotency. As more and more research is done in these areas, it is becoming increasingly evident that with the exception of terminal differentiation cell types, that is, cells which have lost their nucleus and are in the process of dying, all plant cells retain the ability to manifest their full genetic potentialities and produce entire organisms. Does this represent a significant difference between plants and animals? Probably not! It is most likely that the apparent inability of animal cells from later developmental stages to produce entire organisms does not represent the inability of the cell to manifest its potential but, rather, the lack of knowledge on the part of the researcher and his inability to produce suitable conditions for the manifestation of these potentials. In the following chapters we shall consider some of the factors involved in differential expression of a total genotype, that is, differentiation of cell function.

Overview

In this chapter we have considered questions concerning the ability of cells to function in a normal fashion under abnormal conditions. Using numerous selected examples, we have seen that not only the genetic information present in the cell but also the environmental factors surrounding the cell determine its potential and, indeed, that portion of the potential which would be expressed.

chapter four

The Gene—What, Where, and How

The similarities between parents and offspring have been of great interest to man since the beginning of civilization. Numerous theories have arisen to explain the mechanisms controlling heredity, but it was not until the midnineteenth century that a valid theory was proposed. At that time an Austrian monk, Gregor Mendel, designed, performed, and analyzed a series of simple, but critical, experiments.

Until the turn of the twentieth century, when Mendel's works were "rediscovered," the prevalent theories viewed the substance of inheritance as amorphous and fluid, that is, as some type of "blood mixing." Observations in which all of the features of an organism were considered at one time failed to reveal sharp differences between generations, and the conclusion was reached that the hereditary material was constantly being diluted.

Mendel's Experiment

Choice of Material. Mendel succeeded in his experiments with the garden pea where his contemporaries failed because of two major features of his approach: (1) he selected and studied pairs of simple, single-character differences which bred true and (2) he counted, as well as classified, each individual which resulted from an experimental cross. After carefully inbreeding a number of true-breeding seed varieties, he chose seven character pairs to study, all of which showed simple clear-cut differences.

1. Ripe seed form: round (R) vs. wrinkled (r)
2. Endosperm color: yellow (Y) vs. green (y)
3. Seed coat color (flower color): colored (C) vs. white (c)
4. Ripe pod form: inflated (I) vs. wrinkled (i)
5. Pod color: green (G) vs. yellow (g)
6. Flower position: axial (A) vs. terminal (a)
7. Plant height: tall (T) vs. short (t)

Monohybrid Cross—Segregation. He set up crosses, between varieties, for each of the above character pairs and noted that among the first *filial* (offspring) generation (F_1), one character of each of the pairs expressed itself (the *dominant* character, indicated above by an upper case letter) while the other pair member was not at all evident (the *recessive* character, indicated by the lower case letter). In one out of every four plants of the second filial generation (F_2), the recessive character reappeared, not as a transitional expression, but with exactly the same expression as in the recessive plant in the parental generation (P). In addition, there was no difference in appearance among recessives derived from reciprocal crosses. In each successive generation of self fertilization (F_3, F_4, etc.), all of the recessive plants bred true, and one out of every three dominant plants bred true while the other two produced the same distribution— 3 dominants to 1 recessive—in the next generation as the F_1 had in the F_2 generation. Surely, Mendel reasoned, this cannot be due to dilution. The determining factors (the genes) must be particulate, that is, discrete units which are stable through many generations. Furthermore, each plant must carry two units (that is, a pair of genes) for each character. Thus, we must distinguish between the type of genes an organism carries (the *genotype*) and the overt manifestation of these genes in their recessive–dominant relationships (the

Generation	Genotype		Phenotype
P	$RR \times rr$	$[(A + O) \cdot (O + a)]$	Round seed × Wrinkled seed
	↓		
F_1	$Rr (\times Rr)$	$[(A + a) \cdot (A + a)]$	Round seed (× Round seed)
	↓		
F_2	$1RR : 2Rr : 1rr$		3 Round seed : 1 Wrinkled seed

F_2 Summary:

Genotype	Phenotype	Frequency
RR	Round	1/4
Rr	Round	1/2
rr	Wrinkled	1/4

Fig. 4-1. The monohybrid cross.

phenotype). (See Fig. 4-1.) It was easily seen that the behavior of the genes over several generations followed the simple binomial expansion $(A + a)^n$, where n = the offspring generation number (F_1 = 1, F_2 = 2, etc.), A = proportion of dominant genes, and a = proportion of recessive genes (note $A + a = 1$). (See Fig. 4-1, within square brackets, and Table 4-1 I.) The particulate behavior of the genes separating and repairing each generation is the basis of Mendel's first law—the law of *Segregation*.

Dihybrid Cross—Independent Assortment. When two or more pairs of characters were treated simultaneously, for example, round seed with yellow endosperm × wrinkled seed with green endosperm ($RRYY \times rryy$), Mendel found that each pair of characters behaved independently in the double heterozygote ($RrYy$); that is, the presence of either one of the alternative genes from one pair neither enhanced nor precluded the possible presence of either alternative of the other pair (Fig. 4-2). In addition, he found that the relative frequencies of offspring types in the dihybrid cross followed the products of two simultaneous binomial expan-

TABLE 4-1

Generation	Cross	Gene frequency	Offspring genotypes and frequencies
I. Monohybrid cross			
P	$(A + O) \cdot (O + a)$	$1/2\,A : 1/2\,a$	
F_1	$(A + a) \cdot (A + a)$	$1/2\,A : 1/2\,a$	All Aa
F_2		$1/2\,A : 1/2\,a$	$1/4\,AA : 1/2\,Aa : 1/4\,aa$
II. Dihybrid cross			
P	$(A + O) \cdot (O + a) \cdot (B + O) \cdot (O + b)$	$1/2\,A : 1/2\,a$ $1/2\,B : 1/2\,b$	
F_1	$(A + a) \cdot (A + a) \cdot (B + b) \cdot (B + b)$	$1/2\,A : 1/2\,a$ $1/2\,B : 1/2\,b$	All $AaBb$
F_2		$1/2\,A : 1/2\,a$ $1/2\,B : 1/2\,b$	$1/16\,AABB : 2/16\,AaBB : 1/16\,aaBB :$ $2/16\,AABb : 4/16\,AaBb : 2/16\,aaBb :$ $1/16\,AAbb : 2/16\,Aabb : 1/16\,aabb$

46

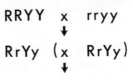

RRYY × rryy
↓
RrYy (× RrYy)
↓

Gametes

♀ ♂	RY 1/4	Ry 1/4	rY 1/4	ry 1/4
RY 1/4	◯ RRYY 1/16	◯ RRYy 1/16	◯ RrYY 1/16	◯ RrYy 1/16
Ry 1/4	◯ RRYy 1/16	◉ RRyy 1/16	◯ RrYy 1/16	◉ Rryy 1/16
rY 1/4	◯ RrYY 1/16	◯ RrYy 1/16	✿ rrYY 1/16	✿ rrYy 1/16
ry 1/4	◯ RrYy 1/16	◉ Rryy 1/16	✿ rrYy 1/16	✿ rryy 1/16

☐ yellow ◯ round

▨ green ✿ wrinkled

F₂   Genotype   Phenotype

RRYY	1/16 **	Round yellow	1/16	
RRYy	2/16 *	Round yellow	2/16	
RRyy	1/16 **	Round green	1/16	9/16 Round yellow
RrYY	2/16 *	Round yellow	2/16	3/16 Round green
RrYy	4/16	Round yellow	4/16	3/16 Wrinkled yellow
Rryy	2/16 *	Round green	2/16	1/16 Wrinkled green
rrYY	1/16 **	Wrinkled yellow	1/16	
rrYy	2/16 *	Wrinkled yellow	2/16	
rryy	1/16 **	Wrinkled green	1/16	

* Breeds true for one character
** Breeds true for both characters

Fig. 4-2. The dihybrid cross.

sions: $(A + a)^n \cdot (B + b)^n$, where n, A, and a are as described above, and B and b represent the dominant and recessive alternatives of the second pair of characters, respectively (Table 4-1 II). (In a trihybrid cross, the offspring followed as the products of three simultaneous binomial expansions: $(A + a)^n \cdot (B + b)^n \cdot (C + c)^n$, etc.) The discrete segregational individuality of pairs of different genes is the basis of Mendel's second law—the law of *Independent Assortment*.

Backcrosses. In addition, Mendel set up two reciprocal types of *backcrosses* in which an F_1 individual was crossed with one of the parental type (P) individuals. These crosses are usually referred to as the *"outcross,"* where the heterozygote (Aa) is crossed with the dominant homozygous parental type (AA), and the *"testcross"* (because it can be used to test for the presence of the recessive gene in a suspected heterozygote), in which the heterozygote is crossed with the recessive homozygous parental type (aa).

Each of these backcrosses produces a 1:1 genotypic ratio of homozygote to heterozygote among the offspring produced, but only in the testcross is this ratio expressed phenotypically (Fig. 4-3).

	A. "Outcross	B. "Testcross"
Genotype	$Aa \times AA$	$Aa \times aa$
Phenotype	[A_] [A_]	[A_] [aa]
	↓	↓
Genotype	1/2 AA : 1/2 Aa	1/2 Aa : 1/2 aa
Phenotype	[A11 A_]	[1/2 A_ : 1/2 aa]

Fig. 4-3. Backcrosses.

Genes and Chromosomes

Nonindependent Assortment. When Mendel's work was "rediscovered," it was soon noted by Sutton and by Boveri that chromosomal behavior during meiosis in gametogenesis parallels the genetic events described by Mendel. Thus, the genes must be located in or on the chromosomes. Mendel's choice of the above seven pairs of characters was indeed fortunate, for the garden pea has seven pairs of chromosomes, and each of these chosen characteristic pairs was associated with a different pair of chromosomes. Bateson and Punnett, in 1906, found two pairs of *alleles* (allele—an alternative gene of a pair of characters; that is, *A* and *a* are alleles, *B* and *b* are alleles, etc.) in the garden pea whose segregational behavior in the dihybrid seemed to contradict Mendel's second law. This discrepancy was explained in 1910 by Thomas Hunt Morgan (who found similar gene behavior in *Drosophila melanogaster*) as a function of *linkage,* the location of two gene loci on the same chromosome. Morgan concluded that the more closely linked two genes are, that is, the closer together they are on the chromosome, the greater will be the departure from independent assortment. Based on Morgan's views, the theory of the linear arrangement of genes on chromosomes arose, and, subsequently, linkage maps of chromosomes were constructed.

Coupling and Repulsion. As we have seen (Fig. 4-2), if the *loci* (locations of genes on the chromosomes) of two pairs of alleles—*Aa* and *Bb*—are on different chromosomes, the F_2 progeny of a cross $AABB \times aabb$ indicate that four types of gametes were present in equal numbers in the F_1 cross. In linkage, however, the F_1 parents produce unequal numbers of the four gamete types. Illustrated in Fig. 4-4 are the two alternative types of dihybrid cross of linked loci— *coupling,* where the dominant alleles for both loci are contributed by one parent, and *repulsion,* where one parent contributes the dominant alleles of one locus and the other parent those of the other locus. In this figure, $m = 1/2$ of the frequency of crossing over (exchange of chromosomal segments between homologues during meiosis), and $2m + 2n = 1$; that is, $2n =$ the frequency of noncrossover gametes,

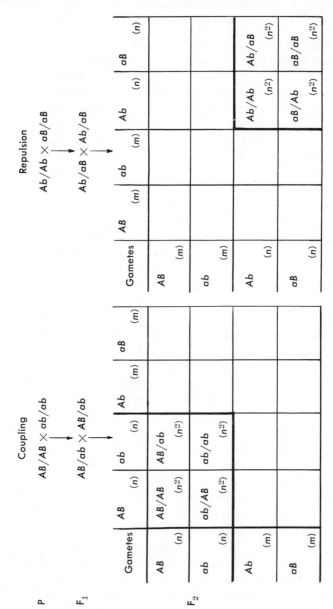

Fig. 4-4. Coupling and repulsion.

and $2m =$ the frequency of crossover gametes. Thus, the frequency of the different F_2 genotypic classes is dependent upon the relative sizes of m and $n,$ and the frequency of the double homozygous classes is dependent upon whether the P generation parents' chromosomes were in coupling or repulsion.

Linkage and Mapping. In a linkage map, the distance between genes is expressed in *map units,* where one map unit equals one percent recombination. An example of an experiment which maps the relative positions of three linked genes in *Drosophila* is given in Fig. 4-5. The female parent in the P generation is homozygous for the sex-linked (genes on the X chromosome) recessive genes y (yellow body color), w (white eye color), and m (miniature wings), while the male parent is hemizygous (the male *Drosophila* has one X chromosome and one Y chromosome, which does not contain the same genes as the X chromosome, and thus forms two types of gametes—one bearing an X chromosome and one bearing a Y chromosome) for the dominant alleles of these genes— y^+ (grey body color), w^+ (red eye color), and m^+ (long wings). The F_1 female progeny are all heterozygous for the three gene pairs, while the males are *hemizygous* (that is, they have only one X chromosome) for the three recessive alleles. (Note: the crossing of the two F_1's in this case is identical to a testcross.) The F_2 ♀ progeny all receive an X chromosome from their father which bears the three recessive alleles. If the three gene pairs are assorted independently, we would expect eight equal classes among the F_2 progeny. If, on the other hand, the three gene pairs were completely linked so that no recombination took place, we would expect only two equal classes, representing the two parental type chromosomes, $y^+w^+m^+$ and $ywm.$ The results obtained indicate that there is partial linkage between these three loci (location of a gene on a chromosome). The progeny are grouped with relation to the number and location

	P	$ywm/ywm \times y^+w^+m^+/Y$
	F_1	$ywm/y^+w^+m^+ \times ywm/Y$
	F_2	(all over/ywm)

Noncrossover class	$\begin{cases} y^+w^+m^+ \\ y\ \ w\ \ m \end{cases}$	3572 2626	$6198 = 0.66$
Single crossover between y and w	$\begin{cases} y^+w\ \ m \\ y\ \ w^+m^+ \end{cases}$	33 39	$72 = 0.008$
Single crossover between w and m	$\begin{cases} y^+w^+m \\ y\ \ w\ \ m^+ \end{cases}$	1607 1501	$3108 = 0.33$
Double crossover class between y and w and between w and m	$\begin{cases} y^+w\ \ m^+ \\ y\ \ w^+m \end{cases}$	9 0	$9 = 0.001$

Total percentage crossing over

Between $\quad y$ and $w - 0.008 + 0.001 = 0.009$
$\qquad\qquad w$ and $m - 0.33\ \ + 0.001 = 0.331$

Observed d-c/o $= 0.001$
Expected d-c/o $(0.009 - 0.331) = 0.003$

Coef. of coincidence $= \dfrac{\text{obs d-c/o}}{\text{exp d-c/o}} = \dfrac{0.001}{0.003} = 0.33$

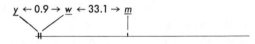

Fig. 4-5. Three point linkage test. Based on data published by T. H. Morgan.

of exchanges or crossovers which occurred in the meiosis of the egg from which they arose. The majority (66%) of the progeny fall into the noncrossover class; in 33%, a single crossover has occurred between the w and the m loci; in 0.8%, a single crossover has occurred between the y and the w loci; and in 0.1%, two crossovers have occurred, one between y and w and one between w and m.

Double Crossovers. Because *double crossovers* represent one single crossover in each of the two regions between the genes being tested, the frequency of double crossovers is added to the frequencies of each of the single crossover classes to obtain the total frequency of crossing over in each of the regions. The number of double crossover progeny is smaller than would have been expected from the product of the two single crossover frequencies $(0.009 \cdot 0.331)$.

The ratio of observed double exchanges to expected double exchanges, referred to as the *coefficient of coincidence,* is a measure of the physical interference imposed by the proximity of loci on a chromosome; that is, if the distance between two loci is small, the presence of one exchange inhibits the formation of another exchange close by.

Sex-Linked Inheritance

As has been mentioned above, the male and female *Drosophila* differ in their sex chromosome complement. The female has two X chromosomes. Thus, in meiosis, the *Drosophila melanogaster* female forms, with respect to sex chromosome content, only one type of gamete, which contains one X chromosome and one haploid set of autosomes for a total of four chromosomes. For this reason, the female is referred to as the *homogametic* sex. The male, the *heterogametic* sex, on the other hand, produces two types of gametes, each having a haploid set of autosomes and either an X or Y chromosome. If a Y-bearing sperm fertilizes a normal egg, the sex of the zygote will be male; if an X-bearing sperm fertilizes the egg, a female zygote will result. The X and Y chromosomes differ greatly in their genetic make up, the Y being relatively devoid of genes (save for fertility factors), while the X has numerous loci and is comparable in gene content to the autosomes. This *nonhomology* of the X and Y chromosomes produces a pattern of inheritance at odds with that of the autosomes, a so-called *sex-linked inherit-*

P	w/w ♀	×	$w+/Y$ ♂
	(White eye)		(Red eye)
		↓	
F_1	$w/w+$ ♀	×	w/Y ♂
	(Red eye)		(White eye)
F_2	♀ w/w $w/w+$		♂ w/Y $w+/Y$
	(1 White : 1 red)		(1 White : 1 red)

P	$w+/w+$ ♀	×	w/Y ♂
	(Red eye)		(White eye)
		↓	
F_1	$w+/w+$ ♀	×	$w+/Y$ ♂
	(Red eye)		(Red eye)
F_2	♀ $w+/w+$ $w/w+$		♂ $w+/Y$: w/y
	(1 : 1)		(1 Red : 1 white)
	(All red eyed)		

Fig. 4-6. Sex-linked inheritance, reciprocal crosses.

ance. This pattern is clearly seen if we compare reciprocal crosses, that is, crosses in which the genotypes of the parents are reversed (Fig. 4-6). Since the males are hemizygous, they always show, phenotypically, the sex-linked genes they carry. Note the "criss-cross" pattern that hemizygosity imposes (Fig. 4-6). The F_1 male progeny are phenotypically identical to their mothers, and the F_2 male progeny similarly indicate the X chromosome constitution of their F_1 mothers.

Nondisjunction

The sex-linked inheritance pattern was a strong piece of evidence for the localization of genes on chromosomes, because the unequal genetic events here manifested were paralleled by cytological inequality. Indeed, an abnormal segregation in meiosis provided Calvin Bridges a means to prove this association between genes and chromosomes. Bridges noted that among every 10,000 F_1 progeny from crosses w/w × $w+/Y$, 4 or 5 had unexpected eye colors. Studying the exceptional flies and their progeny genetically and cytologi-

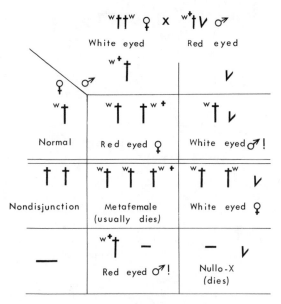

Fig. 4-7. Primary nondisjunction.

cally, he deduced that the exceptions were the result of a meiotic accident. This accident, *nondisjunction*, is a failure of the X chromosomes to separate (disjoin) in meiosis and leads to the production of two types of exceptional eggs (Fig. 4-7): those carrying two X chromosomes and those carrying no X chromosome. When fertilized by an X bearing sperm, the XX egg forms an XXX 2A (2A = diploid set of autosomes) zygote, an abnormal fly referred to as a *metafemale,* which usually dies; the *nullo-X* egg forms an XO (O = no additional sex chromosome) zygote, a sterile but phenotypically normal male with eyes the same color as those of his father. When fertilized by a Y bearing sperm, the XX egg produces an XXY zygote, a phenotypically normal female with eyes the same color as those of her mother; the O egg produces an OY zygote which dies for the lack of

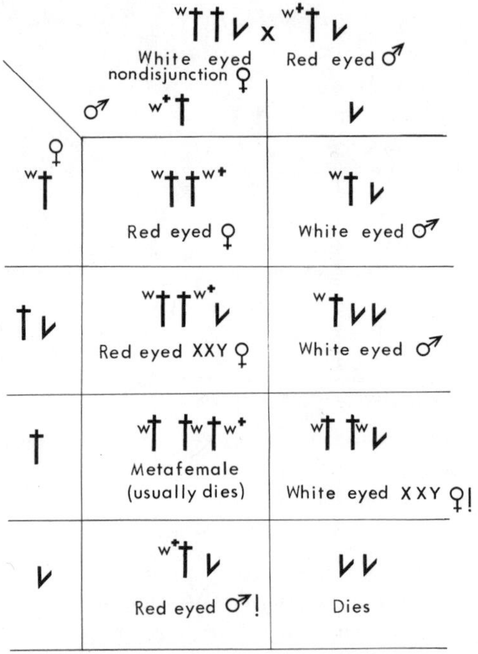

Fig. 4-8. Secondary nondisjunction.

an X chromosome. Since pairing is by twos in meiosis, an XXY female produced by primary nondisjunction will also manifest nondisjunction, so-called secondary nondisjunction, in the eggs she produces (Fig. 4-8). Here again, flies with exceptional eye colors (indicated by ! in Fig. 4-7) and XXY females are produced. The correspondence between abnormal chromosome complements and exceptional phenotypes, Bridges concluded, is proof of the chromosome theory of inheritance. Six years later, in 1922, Morgan found another exceptional case of sex-linked inheritance, one in which nondisjunction always occurred. In this case, he found that the two X chromosomes were attached physically and behaved as one chromosome in meiosis. Females with these attached X chromosomes (XXY; XX = attached X's) (Fig. 4-9), when mated to normal males, produced female progeny identical to the mother and male progeny identical to the father for all sex linked traits.

DNA and the Gene

To this point we have answered questions concerning what the gene is, in a gross functional sense, and where the gene is located. Let us now shift our attack and inquire into the chemical nature of the gene and its chemical mode of action. Although most of the answers to these questions have been obtained from experiments with microorganisms, there is no reason to believe the basic structures and functions differ from those of multicellular organisms. The reasons for considering that the action of the genes is chemical will be presented in the next chapter. As it will be seen, the development of a phenotypic character depends upon the presence and interaction of numerous biochemical substances, most important of which are the proteins. The proteins, although they have only twenty-odd amino acid building blocks, represent a fantastically complex and di-

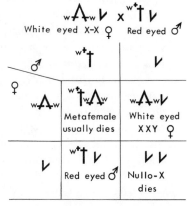

Fig. 4-9. Attached X nondisjunction.

verse group of molecules in both size and configuration. Early geneticists assumed that the protein component of the chromosomes must be the genetic component, for while it was complex and diverse, the other major component, the nucleic acids, were simple and apparently chemically uniform. How, they asked, could the nucleic acids, which are long polymers of four or five nucleotide building blocks, possibly contain enough information in their simple structure to control the multitude of complex functions of the organism? And so, logically, they reasoned it was impossible, and ceased to consider the nucleic acids. The results from two lines of research in the middle of the 20th century brought the nucleic acids back into consideration as the genetic material.

Transformation and DNA. One of these lines centers about work with *Pneumococcus*. In 1944, Avery, Macleod, and McCarthy became interested in an experiment performed by Griffith in 1928, in which he injected mice with a mixture of a dead virulent strain of *Pneumococcus* and a live nonvirulent strain which was derived from the virulent strain. While mice injected with only one or the other of the above survived, those injected with the mixture died of bacteremia, the bacteria recovered from their bodies being of the virulent type. The distinguishing feature between the virulent and nonvirulent strains is the presence of a polysaccharide capsule surrounding the virulent cells. The production of capsular polysaccharide is genetically controlled. Thus, Griffith's results indicated the occurrence of a directed *mutation* (heritable change in the gene). Avery and his co-workers wanted to know what was present in the dead virulent cells (strain SIII) that was able to mutate the nonvirulent strain (strain RII) and thus transform it into a type III strain (like SIII). If they could isolate the "*transforming principle*" (active substance) and produce the change in *in vitro* experiments, they reasoned, they might be able to chemically identify the gene. They proceeded to redo Griffith's experiment *in vitro,* using the presence of the capsule as an indication of virulence. When cultured on a nutrient agar surface, capsulated cells produced smooth colonies (S) while noncapsulated cells produced rough colonies (R). The results of their experiments are summarized in Table 4-2. When RII cells were cultured alone, they gave

TABLE 4-2

Cultured	*Colonies Recovered*
RII	RII
SIII	SIII
Heat-killed SIII	None
RII + Heat-killed SIII	RII + SIII
RII + Gross Extract of SIII	RII + SIII
RII + SIII Capsule Polysaccharide	RII
RII + SIII Protein Extract	RII
RII + SIII DNA Extract	RII + SIII

rise to RII colonies; SIII alone, to SIII colonies. The heat-killed SIII cells produced no colonies alone, but, when mixed with live RII cells, some SIII colonies were recovered. The intact dead SIII cells were not necessary for the transformation, for when a gross extract was fractionated only one component was found to be active—the DNA (deoxyribonucleic acid) fraction. These results were surprising, for surely if the genes were not proteins at least the polysaccharide fraction should have been active in affecting a change in the polysaccharides of the recipient strain. After careful analysis and consideration, Avery, MacLeod, and McCarthy concluded that (1) DNA molecules are themselves capable of carrying genetic information or acting as specific mutagens of the recipient's genes, and (2) the hereditary material may be quite dissimilar from the materials whose production it controls.

Phage Component Labeling. The other line of research which pinpoints DNA as the genetic material involves two studies on viruses. The *bacteriophage,* a virus which attacks bacteria, is an extremely small organism, 60×100 mμ, and has only two chemical components: a protein sheath and a DNA core. Hershey and Chase wondered if the constituent of the phage which enters the bacterium to accomplish infection, that is, phage replication, could be identified. By labeling the phage DNA with P^{38} (radioactive isotope of phosphorus) in one series of experiments and the phage protein coat with S^{35} (radioactive isotope of sulfur) in another series, they were able to trace the components in the infection process. They had discovered that if bacteria and phage were mixed, incubated for 10 minutes, and then placed in a Waring Blendor, the phage particles were separated from the bacteria, but infection proceeded normally. When bacteria were infected with phage whose DNA was labeled with P^{32}, almost all of P^{32} was recovered with the bacteria after blender treatment. With bacteria infected with S^{35} labeled phage, most of the S^{35} was found in the supernatant after blender treatment, that is, associated with the phage particles. They concluded from this that the DNA core was necessary for transmission of phage genetic information to the infected bacterium.

RNA Viruses. The other viral studies which gave similar results are those of Fraenkel-Conrat and of Schramm with Tobacco Mosaic Virus (TMV). TMV is also composed of protein and nucleic acid, but, in this virus, the nucleic acid is RNA (ribonucleic acid). These workers were able to remove the protein sheath without damaging the nucleic acid core. They found that the RNA core material was infectious by itself, while the protein sheath was not. In addition, they were able to combine TMV RNA with the sheath protein from a different virus, which ordinarily is not able to infect tobacco, and from this mixture reconstitute intact virus particles which were able to infect tobacco and produced new normal TMV virus particles. Thus, they concluded, the nucleic acid determines the phage to be reproduced, and it must represent the genetic material.

The Nucleic Acids

Components. These examples are but a few of the many experiments which indicated that the nucleic acids (usually DNA, but in a few viruses RNA) were the genetic material. Let us then ask questions concerning the nature and the location of DNA and RNA in the cells of higher organisms. Both DNA and RNA are composed of residues of two each of two classes of nitrogeneous bases (purines and pyrimidines), a pentose sugar (ribose or deoxyribose) and phosphate groups (Fig. 4-10).

Molecular Structure. While DNA and RNA both have the two pyrimidines adenine and guanine (Fig. 4-10a), they have only one purine in common—cytosine. The other purine in DNA is thymine, which in RNA is replaced by uracil (Fig. 4-10a). The sugar in RNA is ribose, in DNA, deoxyribose (Fig. 4-10c). The monomer of the nucleic acid long-chain polymer is the nucleotide—one nitrogenous base + one sugar + one phosphate pentose. The DNA molecule, as worked out by Watson and Crick, is a double helix, that is, two intertwined connected chains, in which adenine pairs always and only with thymine, while guanine pairs with cytosine. A segment of such a double chain is shown in Fig. 4-11. One feature of such a helix is that while one chain ascends the other descends; that is, the two chains have reversed polarity. Another feature is that they are *complementary,* thus one chain determines the sequential structure of the other. We could make the analogy here between the DNA helix and a ladder which has four kinds of rungs:

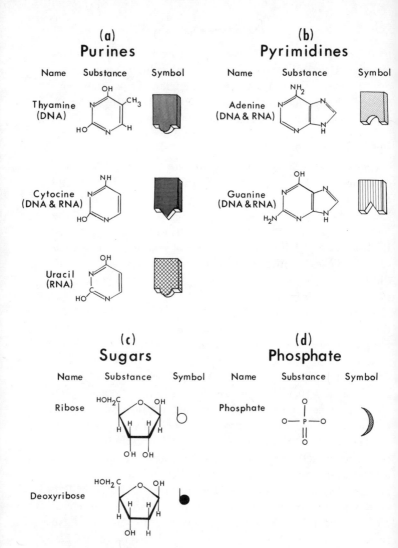

Fig. 4-10. Components of the nucleic acids. (Modified from *General Zoology*, by Goodnight, Goodnight and Gray, 1964, Reinhold, N.Y.)

A–T, T–A, C–G, and G–C, an important feature to which we shall return. RNA may or may not form a double helix and is sometimes found as a branched chain.

Location in Cell. This, then, is basically the structure of the nucleic acids. Where are they found? In higher organisms DNA is found almost exclusively in the nucleus. Here it is combined with certain basic proteins, such as histones, to form nucleoproteins. We can localize DNA more specifically in the chromosomes in the nucleus of all cells. RNA can be found in the nucleus (in the chromosomes, the nucleolus, and free in the nucleoplasm) and in the cytoplasm (free and in the ribosomes). Moreover, while all the DNA found is in the form of long chains, there are several different length RNA chains found in the cells of higher organisms.

DNA and Coding. The nuclear localization of DNA along with the experimental results described above strongly suggest DNA is the genetic material of the higher organism. How, then, can these simple molecules allow for the precise replication of the genes and contain the vast quantity of information they convey? To answer these questions let us return to the Watson-Crick model of the DNA molecule. As we have seen, the double helix is made up of two complementary chains. The complementary structure of the DNA molecule provides the mechanism for precise replication. If the two chains (P and Q in Fig. 4-12) unwind and separate and then the polymerization of the new replicates (p and q) is accomplished by using the old chain as a template, we have a precise *semiconservative replication* (that is, we save one intact old chain and it is found in the new double helix) which should have a stability similar to that of the genes. As for the information of the genes, a DNA molecule could be considered as a sentence made of words formed from a four letter alphabet. If the information of the gene is in the DNA molecule, it must be coded, for the

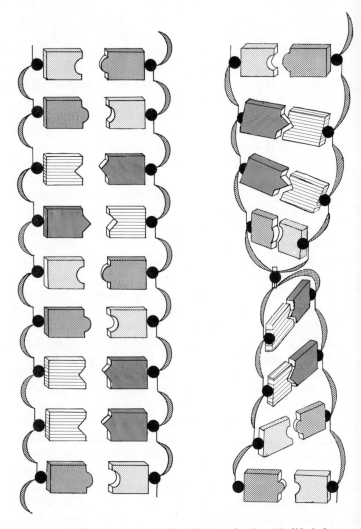

Fig. 4-11. The structure of the DNA molecule. (Modified from *General Zoology*, by Goodnight, Goodnight and Gray, 1964, Reinhold, N.Y.)

overall structure of DNA is uniform. Since, as we have mentioned, the gene is involved with the synthesis of proteins, and since proteins represent, in their primary structure, linear combinations and arrangements of the 20-odd amino acids, it is logical to conclude that the coded message of the gene must be in the form of "words" which determine the order of particular amino acids. If this is so, what is the minimum number of letters each word must have so that each of the amino acids has at least one word? With our four letter alphabet we see that there are only four one-letter words (that is, 4^1 combinations of our letters taken one at a time). Similarly, there are 16 (4^2) two-letter words and 64 (4^3) three-letter words. As we need at least 20 different words to code the 20 amino acids, the code words must be at least three letters long. Let us consider a segment of a single chain of a hypothetical DNA molecule (Fig. 4-13a) containing 12 bases. Assuming the code to be commaless, that is, without spacer words between each sense word, and to be made of three letter words, then there are two ways in which this coded message could be read: (1) as overlapping words (Fig. 4-13b), or (2) as nonoverlapping words (Fig. 4-13c). If the words are read in an overlapping fashion, then each nucleotide, C, appears in three words: GTC, TCG, and CGA (Fig. 4-13b). On the other hand, if the code is nonoverlapping, C appears in only one word, GTC (Fig. 4-13c). Can we distinguish between these possibilities? Yes, because the smallest mutational change in the DNA molecule which would manifest itself as an altered protein molecule is the substitution of one base for another in the molecule (viz., substituting an A for the C), the resulting changes in the protein should distinguish between the possibilities. In the overlapping code this single substitution produces three altered words: GTA, TAA, and AGA, which would manifest themselves in the product proteins as three different amino acids. The nonoverlapping code would produce only a single

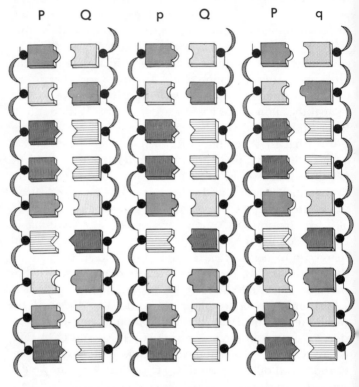

Fig. 4-12. DNA semiconservative replication. (Modified from *General Zoology,* by Goodnight, Goodnight and Gray, 1964, Reinhold, N.Y.)

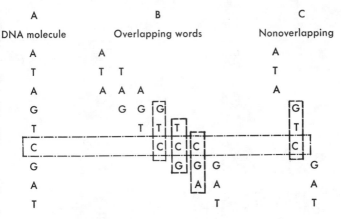

Fig. 4-13. DNA coding.

amino acid substitution, since only one word, GTA, has changed. Indeed, it has been found that all single point mutations in which a mutant molecule is produced show a single amino acid substitution. This suggests that a non-overlapping code is involved in genetic coding.

RNA, Transcription, and Synthesis. Having provided for encoding of a message in the DNA, the question arises as to how this information, which is limited to the nucleus, is transported to the sites of synthesis in the cytoplasm. RNA fills the vital role of message transport. As we have mentioned, RNA molecules come in several sizes. There are long RNA molecules, produced in the nucleus, whose length is comparable to that of the DNA molecules. It has been hypothesized that, in a fashion similar to the replication of DNA molecules, and RNA transcription molecule could be formed using the DNA molecule as a template (Fig. 4-14). Having such a transcription, referred to as *messenger RNA* (mRNA), how is the instruction in the genetic message translated into a protein molecule? To explain this mechanism we must consider two more classes of RNA:

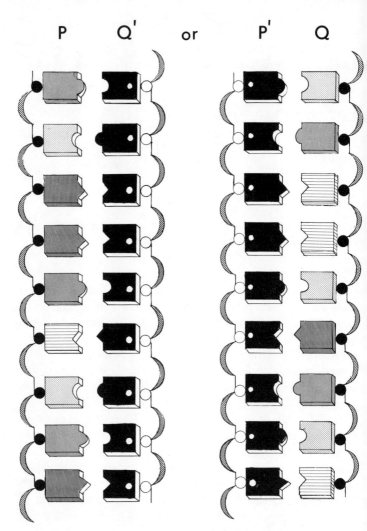

Fig. 4-14. DNA to RNA transcription. (Modified from *General Zoology*, by Goodnight, Goodnight and Gray, 1964, Reinhold, N.Y.)

(1) the *ribosomes,* usually associated with the endoplasmic reticulum, which are the sites of protein synthesis, and (2) a group of small RNA molecules, the so-called soluble or *transfer RNA's* (sRNA), of which there are at least 20 kinds, each type of sRNA molecule attached to a specific amino acid molecule. The messenger RNA leaves the nucleus, enters the cytoplasm, and associates with one or more ribosomes (Fig. 4-15). One end of each sRNA–amino acid complex has a triplet of nucleotides which can pair with the complementary triplet in the messenger RNA molecule. In this triplet by triplet fashion, the genetic message is translated— when two sRNA amino acid complexes are associated with adjacent three letter words on the messenger RNA, a peptide bond is formed between their amino acids. As this linear polypeptide is formed, the sRNA's release their hold on their amino acids and break their complementary pairing with the template RNA molecule. When the linear protein molecule is completed, it is free to fold and crosslink internally so that its final three dimensional structure may be completed. The precise folding is controlled by the linear order of amino acids which is controlled by the encoded genetic message.

Overview

In this chapter we have considered questions about the basic genetic system in general terms—what it is, where its components are located, how these behave as hereditary units, and how they function as cellular control elements.

In the next chapter we shall examine the mechanisms of gene action more carefully and place it in the context of the developing organism.

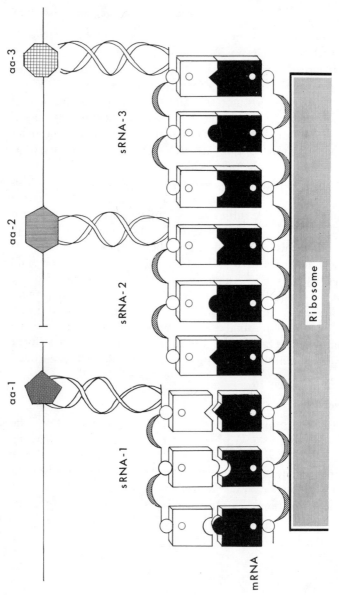

Fig. 4-15. RNA to Protein Translation.

chapter five

Gene Action

In the last chapter we concerned ourselves with the basic mechanics of the gene, with its mode of replication, and with mechanisms of information transfer. Let us now examine the gene and its role as a functional unit in a metabolic system.

We will first ask what the primary action of the gene is. Surely the phenotypic manifestation of a gene is but the end of a developmental sequence, during which, at some time, the gene has acted.

One Gene—One Major Function

Genes and Reaction Chains. Extensive studies of the genetic control of biochemical reactions in numerous microorganisms have led to the "one gene–one enzyme" or, to be more precise, "one gene–one major function" concept. In an organism, the metabolic conversion of one substance to another often involves many steps, each controlled by a specific enzyme. If we consider the hypothetical reaction chain by which substance A is converted to substance D with two intermediate metabolites B and C:

$$\rightleftharpoons A \rightleftharpoons B \rightleftharpoons C \rightleftharpoons D \rightleftharpoons$$

we could express each step of such a reaction chain in the general form:

SUBSTRATE + ENZYME $\rightleftharpoons$ (SUBSTRATE–ENZYME COMPLEX) $\rightleftharpoons$
PRODUCT + ENZYME

where the product of one reaction is the substrate of the following reaction. Although each step is theoretically reversible, the reaction is facilitated in the forward direction because the product of each step is removed by the next reaction so that a static equilibrium may not be established. We can rewrite the overall reaction:

Enzymes: x   a   b   c   d

Reactants: → → → A ⇌ B ⇌ C ⇌ D ⇌

Reaction: (1)   (2)   (3)   (4)

In this hypothetical system, there are at least four places at which the production of D could be blocked by mutant genes: (1) the reaction(s) by which A is produced, (2) the reaction converting A to B, (3) the reaction converting B to C, and (4) the reaction converting C to D. If we consider only reactions (2), (3), and (4), we are involved with three loci—A, B, and C—controlling the production of three enzymes—a, b, and c, respectively. Homozygosity for a mutant gene at any one of these loci (that is, *aa, bb,* or *cc*) would manifest itself phenotypically as the absence of substance D. However, each type of homozygote is biochemically distinguishable.

Substrate Accumulation. When an enzyme is missing, the substrate of that reaction accumulates and its presence is evidence of the blockage of the reaction. Thus, as seen in Table 5-1, enzyme a is missing in the *aa* homozygote, and reactant A accumulates. If there are no further blocks in the reaction chain, the addition of the product of the blocked reaction will enable subsequent reactions in the chain to occur. The addition of reactant B to an *aa* homozygote would allow reactions (3) and (4) to take place. Thus (Table 5-1), the effects of a single genetic block are the deficiency of the enzyme controlling a single reaction and the resulting accumulation of the substrate of the blocked reaction, and

TABLE 5-1

Genotype	Enzyme(s) missing	Reactant accumulated	D produced	Reaction necessary to bypass genetic block
A_ B_ C_	None	None	Yes	
aa B_ C_	a	A	No	B
A_ bb C_	b	B	No	C
A_ B_ cc	c	C	No	D
aa bb C_	a and b	A	No	C
aa B_ cc	a and c	A	No	D
A_ bb cc	b and c	B	No	D
aa bb cc	a, b, and c	A	No	D

they can be bypassed by the addition of the product of the blocked reaction. If more than one enzyme is missing, the substrate of the first reaction in the sequence will accumulate, and only the addition of the product of the last blocked reaction will bypass the genetic blocks.

Alkaptonuria and Phenylketonuria. Let us now consider several examples of the reaction chain relationship. One of the first accounts of the accumulation of the substrate of a blocked reaction was made by A. E. Garrod when, in his book *Inborn Errors of Metabolism* (1902), he described the biochemistry of a mutant gene in man. This gene, a recessive, controls the occurrence of a relatively harmless anomaly, alkaptonuria. Homozygotes excrete homogentisic acid (alkapton) in their urine. This compound, which is normally enzymatically broken down in the blood, oxidizes on exposure to air and forms an insoluble black material thereby producing the characteristic black urine of the alkaptonuric. Garrod interpreted this condition as being due to some block in the enzymatic system, which normally degrades homogentisic acid. Indeed, it was later shown that the blood of alkaptonurics lacked the enzyme which converts homogentisic acid to maleylacetoacetic acid

(Fig. 5-1). The reaction blocked in alkaptonuria is only one step in the metabolism of the amino acids phenylalanine and tyrosine. As more inherited metabolic syndromes were studied in man, it was found that several others acted within the same system. In one of these, albinism, no melanin pigments are produced because some one of the reactions by which tyrosine is converted to melanin is blocked. In another, phenylketonuria, serious damage to the nervous system results from the blockage of the conversion of phenylalanine to tyrosine. The accumulated phenylalanine is converted to phenylpyruvic acid (Fig. 5-1) which accumulates and does the damage. Since, in two of these cases, it is the accumulated metabolite, and not the absence of the end product, that is damaging to the organism, it is not necessary

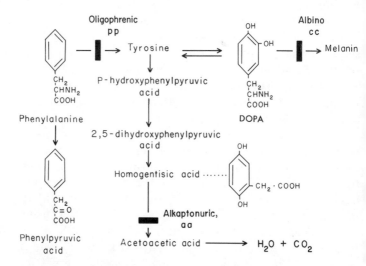

Fig. 5-1. Genetic blocks in the metabolism of phenylalanine in man. (From *Human Genetics and its Foundations,* by Whittinghill, M., 1965, Reinhold Publishing Corporation, N.Y.)

to add the product of the blocked reaction to affect a cure. Instead, it is necessary that substrates of earlier steps be made unavailable so that no accumulation of intermediate reactants will occur. Thus, if phenylketonurics as children are fed a diet lacking phenylalanine, the serious brain damage can be avoided.

These sample human metabolic abnormalities illustrate that the action of a single gene is the blockage of one reaction in a reaction chain. The accumulation of metabolites, and thus the phenotypic manifestation, is characteristic for each step in the chain.

Eye Disc Transplants in Drosophila. A similar example of a biosynthetic reaction chain is found in the synthesis of eye pigments in *Drosophila*. In 1936, Beadle and Ephrussi reported the results of a series of transplantation experiments involving the eye imaginal discs of *Drosophila melanogaster*. In *Drosophila,* as in all Diptera, many of the adult structures, such as legs, wings, antennae, genitalia, and eyes, which first appear during metamorphosis, are developing throughout the larval life in the form of organized cell aggregates known as *imaginal discs*. It was found that these discs could be transplanted from one larva to another and still undergo their normal differentiation, that is, still produce the adult structure they normally produce. When eye discs are transplanted from one larva to the abdominal region of a host larva of the same genotype, the implant continues to develop, and when the host emerges as an adult (*imago*), an eye, of the normal donor color, can be dissected out of the host's abdomen. Thus, the transplantation technique does not alter the normal capacity of the eye disc to produce its own eye color. If discs from wild-type larvae are transplanted into larvae of various strains, each containing an eye color mutant gene (*w,* white; *bw,* brown; *cn,* cinnabar; *v,* vermilion, etc.), or if discs from the various eye color mutant strains are transplanted into wild-type larvae, the

TABLE 5-2

Host genotype	Transplant genotype	Transplant phenotype
+	bw (brown)	bw
+	car (carnation)	car
+	st (scarlet)	st
+	w (white)	w
+	cn (cinnabar)	+
+	c (vermilion)	+
bw	+	
car	+	+
st	+	+
w	+	+
cn	+	+
v	+	+
cn	v	v
v	cn	+

implanted discs usually develop the color of the donor strain, that is they develop *autonomously*. The results of such a series of transplantation experiments, reported in 1936 by Beadle and Ephrussi, are shown in Table 5-2. In these results, there are two notable exceptions to autonomous development. Vermilion discs, in most of the other mutant hosts tested, develop wild-type eye color instead of the expected vermilion color. In a similar fashion, discs from cinnabar larvae develop wild-type color in many of the mutant hosts. When vermilion discs were transplanted into cinnabar hosts, the implant developed the wild-type color. However, when cinnabar discs were transplanted into vermilion hosts, the implants developed the cinnabar eye color. How can these results be interpreted in terms of the reaction chain involved?

Pigment Precursors. We can see that both vermilion and cinnabar are involved in the same reaction chain, and, furthermore, that the vermilion block precedes the cinnabar block. The latter conclusion is based on the fact that v^+ (product of the reaction blocked by the vermilion mutant) substance is present in cinnabar, while the cn^+ substance is not present in vermilion. Thus, the cn^+ substance must represent a reactant derived from the v^+ substance. Wild-type and the other mutants that caused vermilion and cinnabar discs to produce wild-type color must have both the v^+ and the cn^+ substances present in a soluble form so that the implants can take them up and convert them into the pigments necessary for wild-type coloration. The autonomy of the other mutants indicates that they act on a different reaction chain or that the products of the reactions that they block are either insoluble or not produced in large enough quantities to be present anywhere but in the eye tissue itself.

It was later observed that the v^+ and cn^+ substances could be shown to be present in extracts of *Drosophila* wild-type larvae and in extracts of wild-type *Ephestia kühniella* (Mediterranean meal moth). Indeed, the a^+ substance of *Ephestia,* that is, the product of the reaction blocked by the eye mutant *aa* in *Ephestia,* was the same as the v^+ substance of *Drosophila.* The metabolic pathways of eye pigment formation in *Drosophila* have been worked out and are shown in Fig. 5-2. The reaction chain upon which these genes act is the one involved in the formation of the brown pigment, a xanthommatin. Formylkynurenine is the v^+ substance of *Drosophila,* and the a^+ substance of *Ephestia;* 3-hydroxy-kynurenine is the cn^+ substance of *Drosophila.* The eye mutants *st* (scarlet) and *cd* (cardinal) block the reaction after the formation of 3-hydroxykynurenine. The bright red eye color of all of these mutants indicates that they have no effect on the reaction chain which forms the red pigment (a drosopterine). The brownish red eye color of wild-type *Drosophila* results from the simultaneous deposition of the

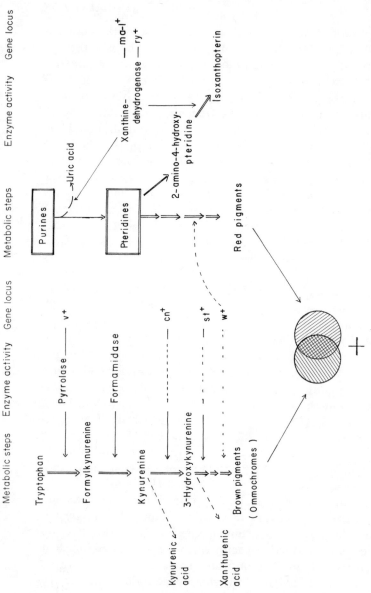

Fig. 5·2. The metabolic pathways leading to wild type eye color in *Drosophila melanogaster*. (Courtesy of Dr T. M.

red and brown pigments formed by each of these reaction chains.

These are but a few examples of the many reaction chains which have been studied in multicellular organisms and have been shown to follow the "one gene–one major function" concept. Let us examine some of the interactions which occur during development that alter the phenotypic manifestation of particular genes. We can divide these interactions into two general classes: gene–environment interactions and gene–gene interactions.

Gene–Environment Interactions

Phenocopies and Chemical Agents. We have already begun examination of gene–environment interactions with our discussion of the nonautonomous eye disc transplants. The body of the host animal was the environment of the developing implant, and the v^+ or cn^+ substances present in the haemolymph of the host were environmental factors which altered the expression of the v or cn tissue of the implant. In a similar fashion, the special diet fed to phenylketonuric children represents an environmental condition altering the phenotypic manifestation of a mutant gene. Vermilion larvae, fed a diet supplemented with formylkynurenine, kynurenine, or 3-hydroxykynurenine, will develop into flies with wild-type eye color. Such individuals are called *"phenocopies"* of the wild-type; that is, they are phenotypically indistinguishable from wild-type although they are not genetically wild-type. It also is possible to create phenocopies of the phenotypes of mutant genes by adding chemical agents to the media in which they are grown. The addition of silver salts to the medium on which wild-type *Drosophila* are grown will cause the adults to have a yellow body color similar to the light body color of the mutant straw (*stw*). The phenotype of the eyeless gene (*ey*) can be obtained by the addition of the phenocopy agent sodium metaborate to the food of wild-type *Drosophila*. Numerous chemical agents are known which will produce developmental abnormalities identical in their manifestations to those produced by mutant genes. One striking example of such a chemical's action in man are the results of recent investigations into the effects of the drug thalidomide. It was noted in Europe in 1960 that there was a great increase in the number of babies born with their appendages reduced or missing. The condition was similar to a genetic condition known to exist in mice, phocomelia, which may also exist as a rare recessive gene in man. The very high incidence of such abnormal births was finally correlated with the use of sleeping pills containing a new drug, thalidomide, by mothers early in their pregnancy. With the withdrawal of the drug from the market, the incidence of abnormal births fell back to its normal low level. These have been examples of chemical factors which interact with the genes to alter their phenotypic expression. Let us now consider some physical factors.

Phenocopies and Physical Agents. We are all familiar with the phenocopy action of ultraviolet light in inducing skin pigmentation. This "tanning" produces a temporary skin color similar to that controlled by certain skin color genes in man.

Heat or cold shocks during embryonic development can cause the appearance of phenotypes which duplicate those caused by known mutants. In *Drosophila,* heat shocks during the proper "sensitive period" cause wing veination defects identical to those found in the mutant crossveinless (*cv*). When green seedlings are kept in the dark for a length of time, *etiolation* (loss of chloroplasts) occurs, and the appearance of the plant is similar to known albino mutants which are unable to produce normal chloroplasts.

Whether or not the agents inducing phenocopies work by the same means as the mutants whose effect they mimic is not always clear. It has been shown in some cases that heterozygotes, for certain morphological mutants which can be phenocopied, are more susceptible to the action of the phenocopy agents than wild-type animals. This suggests that the phenocopy agents are acting upon the same functional system.

Pleiotropy. We have been considering only the environment outside the cell and its interaction with the genes. The cytoplasm itself can be thought of as part of the environment of the nucleus and, therefore, of the genes. We shall return to one aspect of this level of interaction when we discuss control mechanisms. Before we leave the area of gene–environment interaction, let us consider one developmental phenomenon based upon the internal environment —*pleiotropy* or the manifold effect. Often, a single mutant gene alters a number of physical characters which may not bear obvious relationships to one another. There are many examples of such pleiotropic effects. In *Drosophila* the mutant Hairy-wing controls the appearance of extra large bristles (macrochaetae) at various sites on the body, and of numerous small bristles (microchaetae) all over the animal. It also alters the pattern of bristle distribution and the relative dimensions of the thorax and affects the fertility of females. In this case, the causal relationship between the unitary primary function of the gene and the various different phenotypic manifestations is not clear. But in Gruneberg's classic example of pleiotropy, the grey lethal of the rat, the massive syndrome of physical anomalies—abnormal trachea, thickened ribs, fixation of the thorax, etc.—can be traced to a single common basis, a cartilage anomaly which affects numerous differentiating organs during development.

Similarly, the many elements in the "Sickle cell anemia-Sickle cell trait" syndrome in man can be traced to an alteration of the properties of the hemoglobin molecule resulting from the substitution of one amino acid for another in the presence of the Hb^s gene.

In each of these examples, the mutant has, by its primary effect, altered the internal environment of the developing organism. This new internal environment, in turn, has altered the phenotypic expression of other gene-controlled elements in the system.

Gene–Gene Interactions

With pleiotropy still fresh in our minds, we might ask if there are instances of gene–gene interaction in which one gene does not grossly alter the environment of another but, rather, acts more directly upon it.

Let us examine from the two major classes of gene–gene interactions (1) modifiers and (2) control genes.

Modifiers

Suppressors. *Modifiers* are genes which alter the phenotypic expression of other genes. We can usually subdivide this class of genes into two subclasses—suppressors and enhancers. There is a gene in *Drosophila, su^{s2}-v-pr* (suppressor of vermilion and purple), which, when present along with either the sex-linked mutant vermilion (*v*) or the autosomal purple (*pr*), causes the wild-type eye color to appear. This *suppressor* does not mutate the vermilion or purple genes, but rather, enables the genetic blocks to be bypassed. The phenotype of the suppressor in the absence of vermilion or purple bears no apparent relationship to its action in their presence. Most suppressor genes, like *su^{s2}-v-pr,* are specific in their action and are thus limited in their suppression ability to certain alleles at one or two loci.

There was a suppressor of Hairy-wing (*Su^2-Hw*) discovered which was able to alter the expression of certain alleles at at least eight separate loci and, when present alone, produced an altered phenotype not related in appearance to the phenotypes it suppressed. Many studies of suppressor genes in microorganisms have been made, and the only generalization that can be reached at present is that suppressor genes can work in many ways to relieve those blocks caused by mutants. The specificity of most suppressors indicates that they may provide a mutable alternative to back mutation for eliminating the effects imposed by deleterious mutants and thus enable the organism, by means of a second mutation, to bypass these effects.

Enhancers. *Enhancers* or *intensifiers,* like suppressors, alter the expression of genes at other specific loci, but in this case they intensify the expression. In maize, anthocyanin production is determined by a number of genes. This anthocyanin production can be intensified by the presence of the dominant gene *B.* It is sometimes found that a suppressor of one system can act as an enhancer of another, apparently unrelated system. Two genes which suppress the mutant purple (*p*) in *Drosophila,* su^B-*pr* and su^S-*pr,* also act as enhancers of Hairy-wing.

There are numerous genes of small individual effect, *polygenes,* active in quantitative inheritance, that is, the mode of control involved in the development of most morphological characters. It is possible that many of these polygenes act as inhibitors or enhancers of other polygenes and by these means produce their additive effects on the phenotype.

Epistatic and Complementary Genes. Epistatic and complementary genes can also be included in the general class of modifier genes. These two classes are recognized by the way they alter F_2 phenotypic ratios. When dominant alleles from two loci must be present for the phenotype to be expressed, such genes are said to show dominant *complementarity.* In the complex gene control system for aleurone coloration in *Zea mays* (maize), there are two loci which show such complementarity. At least one dominant allele, *C,* must be present in order for any aleurone pigment to be formed. In

P	CC rr (Colorless)	× ↓		cc RR (Colorless)
F$_1$	Cc Rr (Red)	× ↓		Cc Rr (Red)

♀ \ ♂	CR	Cr	cR	cr
CR	cc RR (Red)	CC Rr (Red)	Cc Rr (Red)	Cc Rr (Red)
Cr	CC Rr (Red)	CC rr (Colorless)	Cc Rr (Red)	Cc rr (Colorless)
cR	Cc RR (Red)	Cc Rr (Red)	cc RR (Colorless)	cc Rr (Colorless)
cr	Cc Rr (Red)	Cc rr (Colorless)	cc Rr (Colorless)	cc rr (Colorless)

C_ R_ Red 9/16

cc R_ ⎫
C_ rr ⎭ Colorless 7/16

Fig. 5-3. Dominant complementarity.

addition, there must be at least one dominant R for the red
pigment to be formed. In the absence of R, that is, in the
presence of rr, no color is formed. The results of a cross
between two different corn plants, each homozygous for
factors controlling colorless aleurone, is shown in Fig. 5-3.
The F$_1$ from this cross is colored, and the F$_2$ has a phenotypic ratio of 9:7 instead of the expected 9:3:3:1 dihybrid
or 3:1 monohybrid ratio.

Epistasis, where the condition of one gene alters the expression of another nonallelic gene, can best be illustrated
with an example from the chicken. There are two loci controlling feather coloration. At one locus, the dominant
allele, C, produces pigmentation in heterozygous or homo-

zygous condition, while the homozygous recessive, *cc*, produces no pigment. At the other locus, the dominant allele, *I*, in homozygous or heterozygous condition inhibits color production while the recessive allele, *i*, has no such inhibitory effect. A cross between two different homozygous white fowl (Fig. 5-4) produces all white F_1 offspring and a 13:3 white to colored F_2 phenotypic ratio. In this case *I* is said to be epistatic to *C*.

It should be noted that complementary genes, and indeed all modifiers, could be classified as being epistatic in their action, in that they all represent special classes of the general situation where the allelic constitution of one locus alters the expression of alleles at another locus.

P	CC II White	×	cc ii White	
F_1	Cc Ii White	×	Cc Ii White	
F_2	*CI*	*Ci*	*cI*	*ci*
CI	CC II White	Cc Ii White	Cc II White	Ci Ii White
Ci	CC Ii White	CC ii Colored	Cc Ii White	Cc ii Colored
cI	Cc II White	Cc Ii White	cc II White	cc Ii White
ci	Cc II White	Cc ii Colored	cc Ii White	cc ii White

$\left.\begin{array}{l} C\_\ I\_ \\ cc\ \_\_ \end{array}\right\}$ White 13/16

C_ ii   Colored 3/16

Fig. 5-4. Epistasis.

Control Genes

Mutator Genes. The second major class of gene–gene interactions is of great interest to developmental geneticists. Control genes provide models for explaining differential gene action during development. The first example we shall consider is the *mutator* gene *Dt* in *Zea mays* (maize), described by Rhoades. The dominant allele A_1, in homozygous or heterozygous condition, controls the appearance of purple color; the a_1a_1 homozygote forms no purple pigment. While mutation of a_1 to A_1 is normally rare, Rhoades found that in the presence of the dominant *Dt* (dotted), which is on a different chromosome, the mutation rate of $a_1 \rightarrow A_1$ is in-

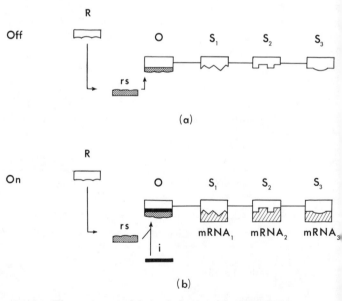

Fig. 5-5. The operon model; i = inducer substance, mRNA = messenger RNA, O = operator gene, R = regulator gene, rs = repressor substance, S = structural genes.

creased. This action of Dt is specific for the a_1 locus. When these mutations occur in an a_1a_1 homozygote during its development, numerous purple spots appear, giving the dotted appearance.

Operon Model. The other gene control example is the *operon* model proposed by Jacob and Monod. In this model, illustrated in Fig. 5-5, genes fall into one of three classes: (1) *structural genes* (S_1, S_2, S_3; Fig. 5-5), which code messenger RNA molecules ($mRNA_1$, $mRNA_2$, $mRNA_3$; Fig. 5-5) for synthesis in the cytoplasm; (2) *operator genes* (O; Fig. 5-5), which permit or do not permit the structural genes to form or release their specific mRNA's; and (3) *regulator genes,* which produce repressor substances that act upon the operator gene to turn it on or off. In our first example (Fig. 5-5a), the system is off, because the repressor substance produced by the regulator gene, which may be located anywhere in the chromosome complement, acts upon the operator gene *O,* depressing its activity and thus not permitting the structural genes to produce their messenger, RNA. However, if some small molecule, an inducer substance, is present in the nucleoplasm it combines with the repressor substance; it activates it and thus allows the operator gene to "turn on" the structural genes (Fig. 5-5b).

Action, Interaction and Time

Integration and Control. In our discussions of gene action and interaction we have viewed most concepts in an "all or nothing" fashion. When we examine features of the differentiating system (in the next chapter), we will become immediately aware of the fallacy of such an oversimplified dichotomous approach. At different times in the course of development of the individual, sets of reaction chains may operate in different sequences. The determination of which reaction chains are acting, and, indeed, the rate of their reaction at any one time in development, depends upon a complex of integrating control mechanisms. Let us examine some of the basic operational components of such integrating mechanisms.

What are the basic requirements for a control system operating at this level? To be effective there must be a way for reaction chains to be turned off when they have completed their synthetic role. This in turn necessitates a mechanism for determining at what point the quantity of a reaction chain's product is sufficient for the proper functioning of the next reaction chain in the sequence. And finally, there must be a way to turn on the next reaction chain.

Feedback Control. Systems in which the end product modulates the reaction chain that gave rise to it are known as *feedback systems*. Of particular interest are the negative feedback systems, where the product slows down the reaction producing it. We have all seen this type of system operating in the automatic volume controls (AVC) of radio and television receivers. There is an equilibrium established, such that the quantity of amplification decreases as the output signal amplitude increases, as shown by a simple reaction chain

$$A \to B \to C \to D$$

where the initial step $(A \to B)$ proceeds only in the absence of D, so that once D is produced the initial step is no longer possible $(A \nrightarrow B)$. As in the AVC example, there must be a quantitative as well as a qualitative relation between output and the control mechanism; a threshold must be exceeded before control is executed. In the AVC, this desired threshold is determined, and set, by the person operating the equipment. In our reaction chain example, the nature of the $A \to B$ reaction will determine the amount of D that must be present for inhibition of the chain. We now can see how the Jacob-Monod operon model provides all the mechanisms necessary for such differential control in development. If the inducer (Fig. 5-5) is the product of another reaction chain, then the reaction chain shown in Fig. 5-5 is turned on only when the amount of inducer has exceeded the threshold level; that is, there is enough inducer substance present to react with most of the repressor substance. If, in addition, one of the products of the chain, such as P_2 (the synthetic product of $mRNA_2$), interacts with the inducer substance so that it competes with the repressor for inducer substance or combines with the inducer to inactivate it, then the operator will turn the chain off when the level of available inducer no longer exceeds the threshold. At the same time, it is possible for P_3 (the synthetic product of $mRNA_3$) to act as the inducer or the repressor for another operon complex; that is, P_3 is also a regulator gene for another system. While this is only a model explanation, it does serve to emphasize the high degree of interaction and interdependence which exists between reaction chains in development.

Overview

In this chapter we have examined the primary action of the gene and some of the interactions which alter the effects that genes exercise on the phenotype of the organism. It is a logical conclusion from our discussions that the environment, in the broadest sense, is an equal partner with the gene and is of great importance in the regulation of gene action.

chapter six

Differentiation and Organization

One of the most striking features of development is the amazing sequence of changes involved in the transformation of the single-cell zygote to the multicellular organism. This transformation involves an ordered series of differentiations at the cellular level and a reorganization of cells and cell aggregates to form tissues and organs.

What Is Differentiation?

Let us first ask what differentiation is. The term *differentiation* describes both a process and a state—the process of progressive physiological and morphological change and the state of accomplished change at any instant in time. We can observe two phases of the process of differentiation: (a) an *intracellular differentiation* or change within a cell and (b) an *intercellular differentiation,* or a divergent change among cells. The intracellular process is the one we observe as we follow the development of one cell, for example, the maturation of a *Drosophila* sperm, where a characteristic series of progressive changes in one cell is involved. Intercellular differentiation involves the progressive divergence of two or more cells in the population of cells, such as two adjacent ectodermal cells, one of which gives rise to nerve cells and the other to epidermal cells. While the intercellular process is of prime interest in studying the development of multicellular organisms, it is obvious that this process is dependent upon intracellular differentiation to accomplish the changes in each of the cell lines which are divergent from one another. Before we discuss the process of differentiation we should mention the types of changes which mark the transition from a low level of differentiation (undifferentiated cell) to a high level of differentiation (fully differentiated cell) (Table 6-1). We are able to draw some general

TABLE 6-1

	Kinds of Changes	
	Undifferentiated Cell	Differentiated Cell
Function	generalized	specific
Shape	simple	complex
Internal structure	simple	complex
Size	more uniform	more diverse
Responsiveness	great	lessened
Motility	great	depressed
Mitotic activity	great	depressed
Quantity of cell products	small	large
Type of cell products	simple (nonspecific)	special (specific)
Metabolism	generalized	specialized
Microenvironment	simple	complex
Cell number	small	large
Tissue architecture	simple	complex
General capacities	great (diverse)	small (restricted)

From Introduction to Cell Differentiation, by Spratt, N. T., 1964, Reinhold Publishing Corp., N.Y.

conclusions from Table 6-1 concerning the nature and results of the differentiation process: (1) The changes of the cell from a state of structural simplicity to one of complexity involve a progressive loss of general physiological abilities and an increase in specificity of function; (2) With this increase of functional specificity, the efficiency of performance of individual functions increases; (3) There is a progressive increase in the interrelation and interdependence among cells, and, thus, spatial and physiological aspects of the environment become more complex. In general, then, differentiation, although it involves a great loss in the overall capacity of individual cells, enables the greater community of cells, that is, the organism, to accomplish diverse complex activities with a maximum of efficiency.

Intracellular Differentiation

Cytoplasm and Nucleus. The cell is partitioned into two major functional areas—the nucleus, in which the coded information for all of the cell's metabolic mechanisms resides, and the cytoplasm, where the business of metabolism is transacted. It is fitting that we examine first the changes that occur in these two areas of the cell during the process of intracellular differentiation. We will begin with the nucleus.

That the nucleus undergoes a precise series of morphological changes at some time during the life of each cell is an immediate conclusion upon examination of the mitotic process. A nondividing nucleus has an appearance quite different from that of one during any stage of division. But this change in morphology, although associated with a change in cell activity, is only temporary. Can we find more permanent changes in the appearance of the nucleus and of the chromosomes therein?

Chromatin Diminution. A striking nuclear change is observed in the early cleavage divisions of a parasite of the horse, the nematode *Ascaris megalocephala (Parascaris equorum)*. There is one pair of chromosomes in a zygote of an *Ascaris* of the race *univalens*. After the first cleavage the chromosomes of one of the two blastomeres undergoes *"chromatin diminution,"* a process in which the heterochromatic ends of the chromosomes are lost during the second division, and the remainder of the chromosome becomes fragmented into a fixed number of segments, each of which then behaves as a separate chromosome in subsequent mitoses. In the division of the cell in which diminution has occurred, two

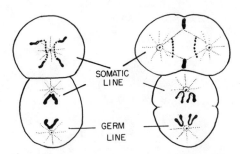

Fig. 6-1. Chromatin diminution in the early development of *Ascaris*. (From *Introduction to Cell Differentiation,* by Spratt, N. T., 1964, Reinhold Publishing Corp., N.Y., based on figures by Boveri.)

daughter cells are produced, each having a number of small chromosomes (Fig. 6-1), while the other blastomere gives rise to two cells each having one pair of large chromosomes. One of these latter cells will undergo diminution during the next division, so that there is only one cell with two chromosomes. This undiminished cell gives rise to the germ cells, all of which have one pair of chromosomes. The cells which have undergone diminution form the somatic cells. Thus, in this animal, nuclear differentiation is marked by a permanent change in the appearance of the nucleus, and this change occurs in cells at the earliest stages of cleavage.

Polytene Chromosomes. The nuclei of the cells of the larval salivary gland in the Diptera (true flies) exhibit a different type of morphological change. During the larval instars, the chromosomes of these cells become *polytene* (many stranded) as the result of repeated chromosomal replications without the accompanying nuclear divisions. In the mature larva of *Drosophila,* over 1000 replicated strands are associated in parallel array to give the characteristic giant

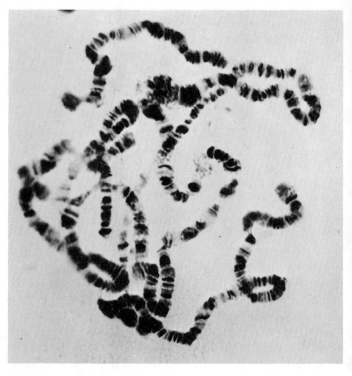

Fig. 6-2. Giant chromosomes from the salivary glands of *Drosophila*. (Photograph courtesy of Dr. E. B. Spiess.)

chromosome, as shown in Fig. 6-2. We can see that nuclear morphology does change.

Change in Nuclear Function

What of functional changes in the nucleus? We have already mentioned (Chap. 3) several lines of research which demonstrate such functional changes. The nucleus of the living blastomere in Roux' experiment functioned differently in the presence of the attached dead cell than it would have if the two cells had been separated. Briggs and King performed a number of experiments in which a nucleus from a cell in a later stage of development (blastula, gastrula, etc.) was transplanted into an enucleated egg. They found that, while nuclei from pregastrula cells were able to control the production of normal larvae (tadpoles), nuclei from late gastrula cells produced embryos the majority of which were arrested at the blastula stage. Furthermore, nuclei from later developmental stages when transplanted into enucleated eggs did not produce cleavage. Thus, the later the stage of development of the donated nucleus, the less able is this nucleus to mediate normal development in egg cytoplasm. Both of these examples serve to emphasize the fact that we must consider the cytoplasmic changes which accompany nuclear change. Since the ultimate control of cytoplasmic synthesis resides in the coded information within the nucleus, if the nuclear function is changing, so then is the function and composition of the cytoplasm. In terminal stages of differentiation, these cytoplasmic changes which have occurred are obvious. The cytoplasm of a mammalian muscle cell is quite different morphologically and physiologically from that of a red or white blood cell, although both began as mesodermal cells. We could express the "loss of nuclear totipotency" observed in the transplant experiments of Briggs and King as a loss of ability on the part of the undifferentiated egg cytoplasm to respond properly to the functionally differentiated nucleus of the gastrula cell.

Nuclear—Cytoplasmic Interaction. Which section of the cell —nucleus or cytoplasm—is controlling the other section? In Roux' experiment, the presence of the adjacent dead cell was detected by the cytoplasm of the live cell, and a spurious message was conveyed to the nucleus that the other cell was present and producing its half of the embryo. In Spemann's ligated embryos, the normal development of

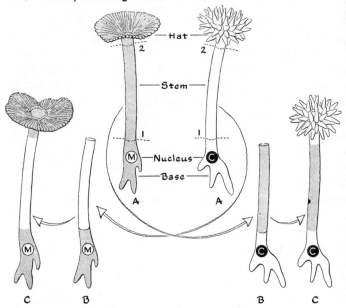

Fig. 6-3. Nuclear transplant experiments in *Acetabularia*. (From *General Genetics* by Adrian M. Srb and Ray D. Owen, San Francisco: W. H. Freeman and Company, 1952.)

the half whose nucleation was delayed was dependent on the "quality" of the cytoplasm and not on basic changes in ability of the nucleus.

Nuclear Control of Cytoplasmic Function. The control the nucleus exercises over the cytoplasm is easily demonstrable. If a cell is enucleated, the cytoplasm may survive for a time, but normal function soon ceases. The mammalian red blood cell is anucleate in its terminal stage of differentiation and, as such, is extremely short lived. The experiments of Hämmerling involving interspecific nuclear transplant in the marine green algae *Acetabularia* provide an excellent example of the functional dependence of the cytoplasm upon the nucleus. These algae are large single cells with a basal rhizoid (containing the nucleus), a long stalk, and a cap. The morphology of the cap is species specific. Hämmerling utilized two species for his experiment: *Acetabularia mediterranea* and *Acetabularia crenulata*. If an individual alga is decapitated, a new cap will develop of the same morphology. If, however, the rhizoid of *A. mediterranea* is grafted to the decapitated, rhizoidless stalk of *A. crenulata* (and vice versa), the cap which develops, after several subsequent decapitations, is characteristic of the nucleus present, not of the cytoplasm from which it developed (Fig. 6-3). Since the rhizoid represents only a very small proportion of the total cytoplasm, the major changes in function of the cytoplasm had to be based upon the mode of control exercised by the transplanted nucleus. As to the question at hand, the answer must be: Neither the nucleus nor the cytoplasm exercises exclusive control over the other.

Although the total potential capacity of the cell rests in the nucleus, the realization of this potential is dependent upon the chemical and spatial constitution of the cytoplasm which, in turn, depends on the proper genetic information for its functioning. In addition, the makeup of the cytoplasm is, in part, a function of the environment. With this reaffirmation of the interdependence between the intracellular differentiation and the environment let us turn to intercellular differentiation.

Intercellular Differentiation

Time and Space. Development is a process occurring in time and space. It is necessary that we view intercellular differentiation within this framework. If the changes in nuclear and cytoplasmic function and morphology are the major consequence of intracellular differentiation, the alteration in time of the internal environment of the organism, resulting from spatial reorganization, is the mark of intercellular differentiation. Thus it is that the control of the

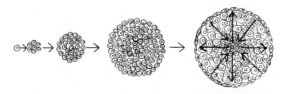

Fig. 6-4. Development of a hypothetical aggregate of cells derived by division from a single cell. Arrows indicate inside-outside graded microenvironmental differentials. (From *Introduction to Cell Differentiation* by Spratt, N. T., 1964, Reinhold Publishing Corporation.)

pattern of development and the development of patterns is the general problem of intercellular differentiation.

Cells as Environmental Agents. First we must examine some of the physical consequences of cell division and cell aggregation. Consider an hypothetical single cell surrounded by a relatively uniform environment. When this cell divides and the daughter cells remain together, each of the two cells is bounded on one side by another cell. As the process continues for a number of divisions, a sphere of cells is formed. The environment of peripheral cells differs from that of cells just below the surface which, in turn, differs from that of cells at the core. There are gradients of metabolites and metabolic products (Fig. 6-4). Waste product concentrations are highest at the core; oxygen and nutrient material concentrations are highest at the surface. It can be seen that the results of this simple organizational change will greatly alter the metabolism of cells in different regions. These metabolic changes, in turn, will further alter the microenvironment and lead to additional functional changes. As individual cells begin to synthesize at different rates, the effects of the products of one cell upon the metabolism of adjacent cells will depend upon the variation of metabolic activity and microenvironment among adjacent cells.

Shift of Control in Development. In the organism, an ordered sequence of developmental events proceeds. The egg is a differentiated cell before fertilization. Its level of differentiation determines the initial cleavage pattern and thereby the primary organization of the embryo. Differential metabolic activity arises as a consequence of nuclear cytoplasmic interactions. Thus, the initial control of differential genetic function is built into the cytoplasmic system. At the time of gastrulation in animals, and of meristem formation in plants, a number of regions arise in which cells differentiate in groups. The metabolism of these regions begins to diverge, and a pattern of metabolite distribution results. The dorsal lip of the blastopore (Chap. 3) is a good example of such a region. The induction capacity of cells from this area may be a result of their specialized metabolism. At this point in development, the control of subsequent organization has shifted from intracellular to intercellular and now rests with the cell aggregate and tissue.

Differential Gene Function

Lactic—Dehydrogenase Isozymes. Both within and between tissues, it is possible to demonstrate progressive change in gene function. Some enzymes are mixtures of *isozymes* (molecules having the same molecular weight but different electric charges). Lactic dehydrogenase in the mouse is such a system of isozymes. Markert and his coworkers have been able to separate from various tissues five different isozymes of this enzyme. The relative amount of each isozyme is dependent upon the tissue and the stage of development. The change in relative quantities of the different isozymes in the mouse heart during pre- and postnatal development can be seen in Fig. 6-5. There is a marked shift from type five to types one, two and three. The lactic dehy-

ONTOGENY OF LDH ISOZYME PATTERNS IN MOUSE HEART

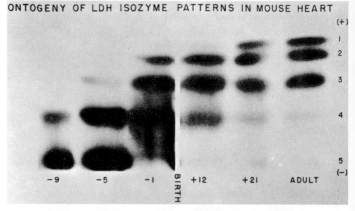

Fig. 6-5. Changes in isozyme patterns during the development of the mouse heart. (From Markert, C. L., and Ursprung, H., *Developmental Biology*, 5:363–381, 1962, Fig. 4, p. 372 by courtesy of Academic Press, Inc., N.Y.)

drogenase (LDH) molecule is a tetramer made of two types of polypeptide chains, A and B, of equal weight. Chain A is made before chain B, and the LDH-5 represents a tetramer of A chains alone. As the B chains are formed there is a shift to production of AAAB tetramere (LDH-4). The production of B continues until some BBBB (LDH-1) molecules are also formed. This shift in the rate of production of the two monomers represents differential gene function within the tissue. The fact that different tissues show their own characteristic distribution of the isozymes is evidence for regionalization.

Adult and Fetal Hemoglobin. Normal adult hemoglobin in man, referred to as Hb^A, is composed of four molecules, two each of two kinds of polypeptide chains, the α and β chains, and is represented as $\alpha_2^A\beta_2^A$. The hemolobin of new born infants (Hb^F-fetal hemoglobin) differs from Hb^A. While it has the same α^A chains, the β^A chains are replaced by γ^F chains so that it is designated $\alpha_2^A\gamma_2^F$. Normally the β and γ chains are not produced at the same time, and there is a switch in the synthesis from γ to β. This switch represents the turning off of the γ gene and the turning on of the β gene at the proper time during development.

Competence and Response

Hormones, Molts, and Metamorphosis. The metabolic products, such as hormones, of one tissue or organ may control the activity and differentiation of specific other tissues or organs. The response of the "target" tissue depends upon the competence of the cells of that tissue. *Competence,* or the capacity to react to chemical stimuli, is a function of the metabolic activity of the cells and the threshold of increase in cell size between molts. Cell division coincides with the molt period. This periodic molt and cell multiplication is controlled by PGH (prothoracic gland hormone, *"ecdysone"*) which is produced by the prothoracic gland when it is stimulated by *Brain Hormone,* a product of neurosecretory cells in the brain. Competent cells, such as epidermal cells, respond to ecdysone by dividing and/or producing a new cuticle. The corpora allata (endocrine glands near the brain) secrete another hormone, JH (*juvenile hormone*), which inhibits metamorphosis and thus promotes continued larval development. When the epidermal cells are stimulated to molt by PGH, the concomitant level of JH will determine the type of new cuticle they will produce. If the JH concentration is high, they will produce larval cuticle. If the concentration is low, they will produce pupal cuticle. If JH is entirely absent, they will produce adult cuticle (Fig. 6-6).

Chromosomes as a Hormone Target. The specific target of ecdysone is apparently the chromosomes of the target cells, for when ecdysone is injected into larvae of the fly *Chironomus* a change occurs in the polytene salivary gland chromosomes which is identical to the change observed during pupation. This change represents *"puffing"* of the chro-

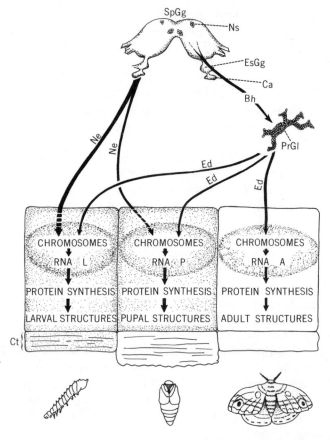

Fig. 6-6. Schematic diagram of the principal endocrine organs of the cecropria silkworm and the sites of action of hormones in metamorphosis; Bh = brain hormone, Ca = corpus allatum, Ct = cuticle, Ed = ecdipore (prothoracic gland hormone), EsGg = esophageal ganglion (corpus cardiacum), Ne = neotenin (juvenile hormone), Ns = neurosecretory cells, Pr Gl = prothoracic glands, Sp Gg = supraesophageal ganglionic mass (brain). (From *Experimental Entomology* by K. W. Cummins, L. D. Miller, N. A. Smith and R. M. Fox, 1965, Reinhold Publishing Company, N.Y., redrawn from Schneiderman and Gilbert, 1964, *Science* **143**, pp. 325–333, by permission of *Science*.)

mosomes (a separation of the many strands) at specific points along their length. The size of the puffs is proportional to the concentration of injected PGH. Functionally, puffing represents an activation of RNA synthesis by gene loci within the puff. When present, JH inhibits those loci which control the production of adult cuticle. Each of these loci has its own threshold for JH, hence low concentration of JH inhibits only certain of the adult cuticle loci and allows for the production of the pupal cuticle, which is an incomplete adult cuticle. It is interesting to note that cells in the imaginal discs have the competence to respond to the very low levels of PGH produced between molts and are thus able to maintain their mitotic activity.

Regionalization

Both hormone production and hormone response competence are regionally determined. The patterned sequence of events during molting and metamorphosis is a consequence of this regionalization. Various mutant genes are able to alter the competence of specific cells or to change differentially the pattern of regionalization. The *Hw* mutant gene in *Drosophila* alters the competence of hypodermal (epidermal) cells to produce bristles and also affects changes in regionalization which result in alternations of thoracic dimensions and the final pattern of bristle distribution. We are better able to demonstrate the effects of single mutants upon this developmental process by a technique known as mosaic analysis.

Somatic Recombination. Mosaic analysis is based upon the process of somatic chromosomal recombination. In somatic cells of *Drosophila,* homologous chromosomes pair during mitosis, and crossing over can occur between homologues after chromosome replication. If a somatic crossover occurs in a $y\ sn^+/y^+\ sn$ cell (phenotypically wild type) of a female *Drosophila* heterozygous for two sex-linked recessive mutants (*y*, yellow body pigment, on one X chromosome and *sn*, singed bristles, on the other), the daughter cells produced after mitotic division is completed would differ genotypically (one $y^+ sn/y^+ sn$ and the other $y sn^+/y sn^+$) and phenotypically (one singed and the other yellow) (Fig. 6-7). If both cells survive and proliferate, they will give rise to

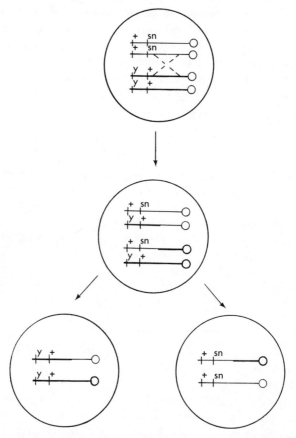

Fig. 6-7. Diagrammatic representation of somatic crossing-over in *Drosophila*.

two genetically different cell lines—each homozygous for one mutant—in an animal whose remaining cells are heterozygous for both mutants. The final result is an animal with two patches of phenotypically different homozygous tissue (twin spots) surrounded by heterozygous tissue. Since somatic crossing over can be induced by X-ray at any desired time in larval development, it is possible to substitute mutant genes for wild-type genes (y for y^+ or sn for sn^+) late in the course of development and compare the results of these substitutions on the final phenotypic patterns. When somatic crossing over is induced in $Hw\ sn/y$ animals, *mosaics* (animals containing tissues of different genotypes) are recovered.

Mosaic Analysis. *Drosophila* has on its thorax, in addition to a large number of microchaetae (small bristles), twelve pairs of macrochaetae (large bristles), located at characteristic positions with one member of each pair on each side (Fig. 6-8). A camera lucida drawing of the lower left portion of the thorax of one $Hw\ sn/y$ mosaic is shown in Fig. 6-9. The position of the anterior dorsocentral bristle (a dc, Fig. 6-8) and the posterior dorsocentral bristle (p dc, Fig. 6-8) are indicated by a and p, respectively, and the y^+

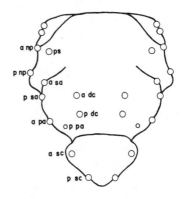

Fig. 6-8. Diagram of dorsal view of the pro- and mesothorax of *Drosophila melanogaster* with the locations of the mesothoracic macrochaetae; a = anterior, p = posterior, ds = dorsocentral, np = notopleural, pa = post alar, ps = presutural, sa = supraalar, sc = scutellar. (From Gottlieb, F. J., 1964, *Genetics* **49**, pp. 739–760.)

$Hw\ sn/y^+\ Hw\ sn$ and $y\ Hw^+\ sn^+/y\ Hw^+\ sn^+$ twin spots by the dark and light shading, respectively. There is an extra $y\ Hw^+\ sn^+/y\ Hw^+\ sn^+$ macrochaeta (indicated by the arrow in Fig. 6-9) between a dc and p dc. Macrochaetae do not normally occur in this position in y/y animals. Its presence can be explained as being due to the increased bristle-producing metabolic activity of the adjacent $Hw\ sn/Hw\ sn$ tissue. This activity enabled the low competence of a y/y cell in the dorsocentral row to be overcome by an increased concentration of some *chaetogenic* (bristle-inducing) substance. This illustration serves to emphasize the dependence of metabolic activity upon the genotype of the cell and of the metabolic activity pattern of one stage of development upon the metabolic activity pattern of the preceding developmental stage.

Overview

Let us summarize what we have said about differentiation and organization during development.

Intracellular differentiation is the result of interactions among the nucleus, the cytoplasm, and the environment. These interactions lead to a specialization of cell function accompanied by nucleo-cytoplasmic morphological changes.

Intercellular differentiation is initially dependent upon intracellular differentiation and upon the regionalization of the embryo into zones having different metabolic activities, that is, a pattern of functional differences. As different regions interact, reorganization occurs, and the large regions subdivide into smaller regions; that is, a new pattern of functional differences arises from the old pattern. This interaction–reorganization cycle continues and results in the orderly process we know as development.

The genotype of the organism determines the total potential metabolic activity of its cells. The types of gene–gene

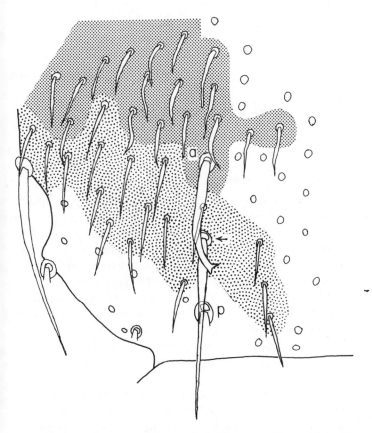

Fig. 6-9. Posterior portion of a mosaic half thorax with an extra y/y macrochaeta in the dorsocentral region; a = anterior dorsocentral bristle, p = posterior dorsoventral bristle, arrow indicates the extra y/y macrochaeta, dark = *Hw sn/Hw sn* tissue, light gray = *y/y* tissue, *Hw sn/y* tissue unshaded, *Hw sn/y* microchaeta locations indicated by small open circles. (From Gottlieb, F. J., 1964, *Genetics* **49**, pp. 739–760.)

and gene–environment interactions which have occurred in a cell will determine its competence at any stage in its development and thus delimit its future changes.

chapter seven

Review and Preview

Questions and Answers

Developmental genetics, as we stated previously, is concerned with the aspects of gene action as they are involved in the process of development in multicellular organisms. Development is a complex series of biochemical, physiological, and morphological events which, within each species, are ordered in a precise sequential arrangement according to a "timetable." Since the genes are the origin of all metabolic potential in the cell, and since multicellularity arises in higher organisms (from a single cell zygote) by a process which involves precise replication of the genome at each step, we have set as our goal the answers to two general questions:

1. How do adjacent genetically identical cells give rise to morphologically and functionally different cell lines?

2. What is the involvement of the genes in the control of developmental mechanisms?

Development, in a sense, is a process without beginning or end. Through this process, each generation is inseparably tied to the preceding and ensuing generations. We began our discussion with descriptions of normal development, for it is necessary to be familiar with the normal process before one attempts to analyze, by means of abnormalities, the mechanisms involved. Our descriptions, although brief and selective, served to illustrate the normal pattern of early development in a number of diverse forms and to display features of the general process of development.

We then focused on experimental embryology. The plan of attack in the experimental approach to embryology is to introduce abnormalities into the developing system and in this way expose features of the mechanisms at work in development. It was evident from our examination of work in this area that both genetic and environmental factors are involved in the process of development, and that some abnormal environmental stimuli enable cells to utilize portions of their genetic potential which are unavailable to them under normal conditions.

The evidence of genetic involvement in development prompted us to examine more closely the hereditary unit— the gene. In a descriptive fashion, we examined the basic genetic system in general terms, considering the chemical nature of the gene, how the gene behaves in heredity, and how it manifests itself in the intact organism. Using examples, we viewed the phenotypic consequences of the general processes of mutation, segregation, and recombination.

Since the gene is a functional unit in the metabolic process of development, we proceeded to examine its physiological action in greater detail. We saw that the primary function of the gene is biochemical, and it is unitary. Examples provided evidence for sequential functioning of sets of genes, that is, reaction chains. These chains require that all of their elements be functional if the normal end product is to be produced. Emphasis was placed on the role of interactions—intergenic, gene–environment, and combinations thereof—as mechanisms controlling the phenotypic manifestations of the individual genetic elements. Example models of genetic control systems were also presented. We were drawn to the conclusion that the environment, in the broadest sense of this term, is the functional partner of the genes.

Having thus laid the foundations, we were able to view the mechanisms of development within the framework of genetics, the organization of the developing organism, and time. We considered intracellular and intercellular differentiation, primary mechanisms in development, and examined them in terms of gene action and interaction in time.

General Conclusions

What general conclusions can we make as a result of our discussions? The orderly succession of stages through which a developing organism passes is accomplished by an orderly succession of functional changes within the organism, the process of *epigenesis*. The operation of the genes is at the cellular level, within what Waddington has termed an *epigenetic action system*. Waddington's model for such a system is shown in Fig. 7-1. In this model, each gene is initially involved in the determination of a primary protein (through the DNA-RNA-Synthesis system we described in Chap. 4) within the *gene–protein system*. The set of processes which connect a gene to its phenotype is the *gene–action system*. The feedback control of these systems is operative at a number of levels. One gene may influence the function of another (Fig. 7-1a). The cytoplasm can act directly upon the gene (Fig. 7-1b), upon the gene protein system (Fig. 7-1c), or upon the processes which convert the primary protein to its phenotypic manifestation (Fig. 7-1d). Intercellular differentiation, then, is a process involving functional changes as a result of interactions within a genetically defined system.

Intercellular differentiation is the process of sequential reorganization which redistributes differentiated cells and triggers new intracellular differentiation. The general problem involved in this reorganization is one of the formation of patterns. The pattern of changes in regionalization, in time, provides the sequence of environments which enables subsequent reorganization. The initial pattern of regional-

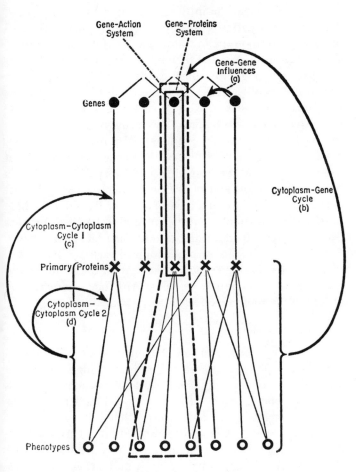

Fig. 7-1. The epigenetic action system of Waddington. (From *New Patterns in Genetics and Development* by C. H. Waddington, 1962 (Fig. 1) by courtesy of Columbia University Press, N.Y.)

ization results from the intracellular differentiation process. All subsequent patterns, including the final phenotypic patterns, depend upon the initial pattern—the differential function of regions within the pattern and the differential interactions among regions—which leads to further divergence in function. It is obvious that there need not be a gene present to control each step in development. The genes exercise their control of development by means of their products, through a system involving differential function in time.

The developmental system can be likened to an industrial complex. Tool makers provide each factory with tools. The nature of the tools and of the raw materials available will determine the parts that any one factory will produce. These parts will, in turn, affect the final product. As the complex becomes larger, the specialization of each factory increases. For efficiency, the rate of production of each factory is controlled by feedback mechanisms, so that all the plants in the complex are temporarily in phase with one another. The genes are the tool makers of cells.

A Word of Caution

We have examined some of the general concepts of developmental genetics. However, before previewing some of the areas of future research, a few words of caution are necessary. Any general survey of a scientific field must, by necessity, omit many examples, theories, and ideas which are found in profusion in the literature. Many theories will be discarded as new knowledge disproves them: others will be strengthened and expanded by new information. This book has attempted to present a foundation for understanding developmental genetics, without novel or daring concepts. The reader should question all ideas presented here, and not accept them blindly.

More Questions

What are some of the questions in developmental genetics for which answers will be sought in the next few years? Although the areas of research are diverse, certain major questions will need answers.

On the level of the cell and its components, the question of the reversibility of differentiation arises. In plants it is known that most cells are able to dedifferentiate. This is not true for most animal cells. The nature of the mechanisms controlling this dedifferentiation is being studied in cell and tissue culture and in regeneration experiments.

This problem is related to another major question—how is temporal control of gene function accomplished? The precision of timing of the many steps in development indicates that there could be "timing genes" which act to synchronize the activity of other genes. A clearer understanding of biochemical, physical, and genetic control factors involved in the timing of intracellular genetic activity gives a better basis for interpreting the synchrony of intercellular activity.

What are the factors that keep cells working together and that keep them aggregated; that is, what is the nature of intercellular integration? Individual members of the population of cells comprising a tissue do not behave as free individuals but are integrated into their community, both on the level of metabolic activity and on the basis of physical location. The mechanisms which hold cells together physically and metabolically in tissues are probably related to those mechanisms which integrate tissues in the organism, and therefore, they are of great importance for our understanding of the control of organization in development.

There are many pathways to the wild-type phenotype in most organisms. Indeed, a broad range of environmental changes can be tolerated by a developing organism without altering the final normal phenotype. The nature of the homeostatic mechanisms acting in development will shed light on the latent ability of cells to manifest their total potential, as prescribed by the genes, and thus on the nature of the elements of the feedback control mechanisms acting during development.

While the nature of the gene-action system (Fig. 7-1) will be studied, using many diverse phenotypic characters, behavioral characters will receive increasing attention. The behavioral activity of an organism is intimately related to its genetic constitution. The nature of genetic control of the behavioral phenotype is important for a clear understanding of selective mechanisms in evolution for an understanding of the behavior of the organism itself.

These are but a few of the areas to be investigated. The only factors limiting research in developmental genetics are the workers' imaginations and the available techniques for transforming ideas into information.

Selected Readings

"Differentiation and Development, Proceedings of a Symposium Sponsored by the New York Heart Association," *J. Exptl. Zool.* **157** (1), 1964.

Goldschmidt, R., *Theoretical Genetics,* University of California Press, Berkeley, Calif., 1958.

Hadorn, E. (Translated by U. Mittwoch), *Developmental Genetics and Lethal Factors,* Methuen & Co., Ltd., London, 1961.

Sinnott, E., Dunn, L., & Dobzhansky, T., *Principles of Genetics,* 5th Edition, McGraw-Hill, New York, 1958.

Srb, A., Owen, R., *General Genetics,* W. H. Freeman and Company, San Francisco, 1958.

Waddington, C. H., *New Patterns in Genetics and Development,* Columbia University Press, New York, 1962.

Wagner, R., and Mitchell, H., *Genetics and Metabolism,* 2nd Edition, John Wiley and Sons, Inc., New York, 1964.

Willier, B., Weiss, P., and Hamburger, W. B., Editors, *Analysis of Development,* W. B. Saunders Company, Philadelphia, 1955.

Index

Numbers in *italic* indicate figures.